DBT Workbook For Emotional Eating

Stop Compulsive Overeating & Quit Your Food Addiction with Proven Dialectical Behavior Therapy Skills for Men & Women | Stop Binge Eating & Embrace a Healthy Diet

By Barrett Huang

https://barretthuang.com/

Contents

Introduction 7

Who Should Read This Book...11

Goals of This Book 11

Be Patient and Kind to Yourself 12

Chapter 1: Understanding Emotional Eating 13

What is Emotional Eating?...13

Emotional Eating vs. Stress Eating vs. Binge Eating 14

Emotional Hunger vs. Physical Hunger 15

It's NOT About Food...16

It's NOT All About Willpower..18

Emotional Eating: Causes and Triggers 20

Impact of Emotional Eating on Your Mental and Physical Health 22

Mental Health 22

Physical Health 23

Chapter 2: Dialectical Behavior Therapy 101................................26

What is DBT?...26

How DBT Can Be Used to Treat Emotional Eating 27

DBT Primary Concepts: Acceptance and Change 27

Radical Acceptance 27

Worksheet: Radical Acceptance 29

Desire to Change 31

Worksheet: Desire to Change 32

Worksheet: Radical Acceptance + Desire to Change 33

DBT Primary Skills: Mindfulness, Distress Tolerance, Emotion Regulation, Interpersonal Effectiveness 34

Chapter 3: Mindfulness Skills for Emotional Eating 37

Introduction to Mindfulness 37

Worksheet: Belly Breathing 38

Worksheet: Take 5 39

Worksheet: 4-7-8 Breathing 40

Mindful Eating 41

Principles of Mindful Eating 41

Benefits of Mindful Eating 43

Worksheet: Mindful Eating 45

Worksheet: TASTE 48

Worksheet: Wise Mind 49

Chapter 4: Distress Tolerance Skills for Emotional Eating 52

Introduction to Distress Tolerance 52

Stress and Emotional Eating 52

Stress vs. Distress 52

Importance of Distress Tolerance Skills for Emotional Eating 53

Worksheet: Self-Soothe Using Your Five Senses 55

Worksheet: The Grounding Grid 57

Worksheet: STOP 59

Worksheet: TIPP 62

Chapter 5: Emotion-Regulating Skills for Emotional Eating 65

Introduction to Emotion Regulation 65

Practicing Self-Compassion, Self-Forgiveness, and Self-Validation 66

Worksheet: Self-Compassion..68

Worksheet: Self-Forgiveness 70

Worksheet: Self-Validation..72

Identifying the Emotions That Trigger Your Emotional Eating.......................74

Worksheet: Identifying Your Emotional Triggers.............................75

Worksheet: The Happiness Habit 80

Worksheet: Opposite Action..83

Worksheet: PLEASE 88

Chapter 6: Interpersonal Effectiveness Skills for Emotional Eating...................91

Introduction to Interpersonal Effectiveness 91

Importance of Healthy Relationships in Recovering from Emotional Eating ..92

Worksheet: Communicating Boundaries 95

Worksheet: DEARMAN 98

Worksheet: GIVE 102

Worksheet: FAST 104

Chapter 7: Developing Healthy Habits 108

Top 10 Healthy Food and Eating Habits.....................................108

Quick Guide to Meal Planning and Prepping.................................112

What is Meal Planning? 113

What is Meal Prepping?..114

Incorporate Physical Activity into Your Routine 115

Manage Daily Stress through Healthy Coping Mechanisms 117

Chapter 8: Building a Support System......................................121

Cultivate a Supportive Inner Voice (Self)................................121

    Self-Sabotage – What You May Be THINKING 121

    Self-Sabotage – What You May Be DOING.. 122

  Build Your Support Circle (Others)... 123

Chapter 9: Dealing with Setbacks and Relapses 127

  How to Prevent Setbacks 127

  How to Recover from a Setback 130

Chapter 10: Maintaining Long-Term Success 133

  Top 10 Strategies for Maintaining Healthy Eating Habits 133

  Celebrate Progress and Achievements with Non-Food Related Rewards 136

  Reflection and Gratitude Practice 138

    Worksheet: Reflection and Gratitude...139

Conclusion 142

Appendix... 144

  Emotional Eating Self-Assessment Quiz.. 144

  The Clean Your Plate Syndrome...148

    Top 10 Tips to Stop Cleaning Your Plate 149

  How to Establish a Sleep Routine 151

  How to Support an Emotional Eater 154

Review Request 158

Further Reading 159

About the Author..160

Index 161

References 163

Introduction

The bell rings, signifying the end of the school day, and everyone noisily leaves the room. I sense our teacher, *Mr. M*, looking at me, but I avoid eye contact. I walk out of school to a nearby internet café. I buy a bag of chips and a big soda and settle into my favorite corner, where I would stay alone for a few hours. It is getting dark, so I get up and walk home.

As I reach home, I am as quiet as possible because I do not want my family to know I am back. I go straight to my room, close the door and go online to play games (yes, again) or listen to music to pass the time. I reach for my stash of junk food, usually potato chips, and eat until the bag is empty. Often, I am surprised when it IS empty because I do not recall eating so much.

At one point, I hear my dad calling me for dinner. I go down, but since I stuffed myself already, I barely eat. Dinner is unpleasant because my parents are in the middle of a divorce. My sister and I are trying to avoid anything that might trigger my mom or dad to fight. Finally, dinner is over, and I go up to my room.

I listen to music, watch TV, play online, or do whatever homework I need to do. At this point, I would now switch to eating the Chinese pastries and buns my father had brought home from the bakery where he works. I have sleep problems, so I stay up all night and eat. Throughout this time, junk food and pastries are beside me... my constant companion on another day of loneliness.

This is how I spent the majority of my adolescent years. I often felt like I was in a never-ending cycle of despair, boredom, and loneliness. I truly did not have much hope for the future and did not even think about it. Every day, my only goal was to make it through.

Back then, I did not think I was emotionally eating. I was not focused on *how* I was coping. My thoughts were preoccupied with *what* I was coping with.

My parents emigrated from China to Canada in the 1980s to provide a better future for their children to come. (My sister and I were born in Toronto.) Unfortunately, they could not escape their personal mental issues.

My father was a hoarder with undiagnosed Obsessive-Compulsive Disorder (OCD). My mother was constantly worried about something and always expected some disaster to strike at any moment. She had undiagnosed General Anxiety Disorder (GAD). With both parents emotionally absent, I was understandably often anxious and confused. There was just nothing "stable" in my world. This, of course, greatly impacted my everyday behavior and approach to life.

It also did not help that my parents were going through a messy divorce when I was around 11 years old. I was not talking to my mom and sister since I was on my dad's side, and my sister was not talking to our dad and me because she was on our mom's side. My family was torn apart just at the time my sister and I needed a stable and loving environment to help us through our adolescent years.

Unsurprisingly, by the time I was in my teens, I already had signs of OCD and GAD (later, as an adult, I would be officially diagnosed with these mental health disorders by a professional).

My mental health problems wreaked havoc on my social skills. So much so that when I was in high school, I would not have a single friend in a school with nearly 5,000 students. This loneliness made me self-isolate and turn to food to cope. I did not know it then, but I used food to self-medicate.

They say it is better to be mad (show anger) than sad (admit pain). I guess I was doing this because I would rather hide and eat than be seen not having any friends. That would just be too humiliating and painful.

Did things get better for me? Fortunately, they did—for a while.

When I graduated from high school, I went to college and traveled to Asian countries. I spent time in China, South Korea, Hong Kong, Thailand, and the Philippines. I spent three years teaching English as a Second Language (ESL) in South Korea. To this day, I consider it one of the best decisions I have ever made. Living on my own made me independent, and teaching gave me a sense of fulfillment I had never had before.

People say that traveling opens your mind, and I agree. Traveling to different parts of the world and seeing how other people dealt with their challenges (I visited some underprivileged areas) helped me see things from more than just my point of view.

My years away from home also opened my mind to the possibility of "better," something I never thought was possible for me before. Unfortunately, I resorted to my old ways when I returned home to my family.

I did not know what to do with my life when I returned from Asia. So, I stayed with my sister and hibernated on her couch for a year. And guess who my constant companion was during this time? Food, of course.

I ate because I was bored.

I ate because I was lonely.

I ate because I could not deal with all the "family drama" I had left behind for nearly four years.

I ate because my OCD, GAD, and depression were getting worse.

I ate because I was uncertain about the next chapter of my life.

I ate and ate... but nothing became better.

Did things change for me? Fortunately, they did—this time for good.

I always had poor eyesight, and the years spent playing online and watching TV caught up with me. My vision got so bad that I got myself off that couch and got an eye exam, which revealed I had a retina tear. Fortunately, it got repaired, but I got an increase in eye floaters, which affected my vision and quality of life. I became depressed and self-isolated again, with nothing but food as my "friend."

After some time, I started to adapt. I realized that I could do nothing about my eye floaters and that I should start being more mindful about what I eat and put in my body since food affects one's health. Also, I was already 30 at this stage. I was not in my teens or twenties anymore and did not want to spend the rest of my life on my sister's couch. So, I decided to get better.

I contacted a mental health professional who prescribed anti-anxiety medication for my GAD, which jumpstarted my healing process. In addition, I went through psychotherapy, specifically Cognitive Behavior Therapy (CBT). I also dived into many self-help books to learn more about happiness, philosophy, and how to improve myself.

After a while, I felt well enough to ask my doctor to reduce my dosage. (For the record, I continue to take anti-anxiety medication, which helps me manage my GAD.) I also realized that I needed something other than CBT, so I began to look into different psychotherapy methods. I discovered Dialectical Behavior Therapy (DBT), which enables me to finally break free from my unhealthy coping strategies and live the life I never even dared to dream of before.

I still experience bouts of OCD, GAD, and depression occasionally, but these disorders no longer cripple me. **I no longer use food to feel better, either.** I have found the tools to help me deal with my emotions more positively. I earnestly hope you will accomplish the same with this book.

Who Should Read This Book

This book is for anyone who wants to be free from emotional eating. Whether you use food for comfort or reward, this book aims to give you better, healthier ways to cope with life. This book is also for you if you find that your emotional eating has led to food addiction, weight problems, eating disorders, mental or health issues, or if you want to prevent these adverse effects. Finally, this book is for you if you want to control your emotions instead of having them control you.

Goals of This Book

The purpose of this book is to help you get a better understanding of emotional eating and to give you real-life tools to help you better cope with unpleasant emotions.

Emotional eating is very complex, so I sincerely hope this book gives you clarity. Awareness and understanding are critical when dealing with any unhealthy coping mechanism. However, understanding emotional eating is only half the battle; the other half is learning how to cope. This is when the book's second section comes in.

Dialectical Behavior Therapy (DBT) taught me NOT to use food to cope with negative emotions. I will go through DBT in-depth and provide plenty of exercises to help you properly use these approaches.

Be Patient and Kind to Yourself

Wherever you are right now, it did not happen overnight. So have patience and understanding with yourself. Remember that, for the most part, emotional eating is a learned behavior, and it can be difficult to break the cycle. So refrain from criticizing and judging yourself for your struggles. And whenever setbacks happen, as they always do, keep moving forward. Remember, each positive step is one taken in the right direction.

Chapter 1: Understanding Emotional Eating

"Eating your emotions won't make them go away."
—Karen Salmansohn

What is Emotional Eating?

Emotional eating is turning to food in response to emotions instead of eating to satisfy physical hunger or nutritional demands.

When you are experiencing unpleasant feelings, this is usually accompanied by feelings of emptiness. In this instance, you may use food to temporarily fill that emptiness, so food becomes a source of comfort.

Food can also be used in response to positive emotions. In fact, using food as a reward is a common practice in our society. Many of us use food as a way to celebrate milestones or as a way to reward ourselves for accomplishing a task. However, when you do this, it reinforces the idea that food is more than just nourishment for your body. Food is linked to moments of happiness.

Furthermore, using food as a reward can lead to a cycle of restriction and bingeing. For example, you may restrict your food intake during the week, only to indulge in high-calorie foods as a reward on the weekend. This cycle can lead to feelings of guilt and shame, which can further perpetuate the emotional eating cycle.

So, emotional eating is a way for us to deal with emotions rather than fill a hungry stomach.

Emotional eating is different from physical hunger in several ways. When you eat emotionally, you often crave specific foods high in sugar, fat, or salt rather than healthy and nutritious foods your body needs. Emotional eating can also make you eat quickly without paying attention to your body's natural signals of fullness and hunger. You may eat until you feel uncomfortably full, then experience guilt, shame, or regret.

Technically, emotional eating is not classified as an eating disorder in the Diagnostic and Statistical Manual of Mental Disorders (DSM-5).[1] However, emotional eating can be a symptom of an eating disorder. It is important to note that emotional eating is a behavior, not a diagnosis, and should be addressed in the context of your overall mental health and well-being.

Emotional Eating vs. Stress Eating vs. Binge Eating

Emotional eating, stress eating, and binge eating are often interchanged phrases. Although there can be some overlap between them, there are distinct differences too.

Emotional eating is the practice of eating in response to an emotional state. Emotional eaters use food to soothe negative emotions or as a reward for positive emotions and often eat more than they need to feel full or satisfied.

Stress eating, or stress-induced eating, is emotional eating **specifically triggered by stress**. When under stress, people often turn to food for comfort, which can lead to overeating and weight gain over time. However, not all emotional eating is related to stress, and not all stress eating is related to negative emotions.

Binge eating disorder (BED) is defined by recurrent eating sprees, which entails quickly eating enormous amounts of food while feeling

out of control. Binge-eating episodes are often accompanied by guilt, shame, and distress. Unlike emotional eating, which can occur sporadically, binge eating is a consistent pattern of behavior that can interfere with daily life.

Emotional Hunger vs. Physical Hunger

You may confuse emotional hunger with physical hunger because the sensations in the body can be very similar. Both physical and emotional hunger can cause a grumbling stomach, headaches, and feelings of weakness or lightheadedness.

Additionally, you may have been taught to use food as a coping mechanism for uncomfortable emotions, leading you to *automatically* rely on food when feeling stressed, anxious, or upset. This, in turn, can make it difficult for you to distinguish between true physical hunger and the desire to eat as a way of soothing emotional discomfort.

Finally, if you are not in touch with your emotions or struggle with identifying and expressing your feelings, you may find it hard to recognize the difference between emotional and physical hunger.

Following are more telltale signs that what you are feeling is emotional hunger, not physical hunger:

- **Unexpected.** Emotional hunger hits you all at once, making you feel rushed and overwhelmed. On the other hand, physical hunger comes on more slowly. Unless you haven't eaten in a long time, the desire to eat does not feel as strong or needs to be satisfied immediately.

- **Cravings.** When you're emotionally hungry, you want certain "comfort foods." You most likely want junk food or sweet snacks that can give you an immediate rush. Healthy foods, like an apple or carrot sticks, simply will not suffice.

- **Mindless**. Emotional hunger often makes people eat without thinking. Before you know it, you have eaten a whole bag of chips or several slices of cake without really paying attention or fully enjoying it. Eating to satisfy physical hunger makes you usually more aware of what you put in your mouth.

- **Unsatisfied**. Emotional hunger is never really satisfied. You eat for temporary relief, but the "hunger" does not disappear, so you want more and more. As a result, you often eat until you are too full of moving. On the other hand, physical hunger doesn't need to be filled. When your stomach is full, you feel good about yourself.

- **Not related to your stomach.** Emotional hunger is not felt in your stomach. That is, you usually do not experience rumbling or even pain in your stomach. Instead, you strongly desire to eat that will not go away. Your attention is riveted on how certain foods feel, taste, and smell.

- **Leads to sorrow, guilt, or shame.** After giving in to your emotional hunger, you feel bad after eating. Deep down, you know you are not eating because you need nutrients; you are eating to fill an emotional void.

It's NOT About Food

Emotional eating is not about food but about eating in response to feelings. In fact, when you emotionally eat, you may not even be (physically) hungry at all! The problem is that you are trying to apply a food solution to an emotional problem.

Although you may be eating to cope with certain emotions, it is important to note that emotions and food influence each other. That is, emotions can influence your food choices, and food can, in turn, influence your emotions.

For example, you may turn to junk food when dealing with negative emotions because it provides temporary comfort or pleasure. The high fat and sugar content in junk food triggers the release of feel-good chemicals in your brain, such as dopamine, which can make you feel better in the short term. Additionally, you may associate certain junk foods with positive memories or emotions from your past, such as eating ice cream when you pleased your parents as a child. So, when you experience negative emotions, you may turn to these familiar foods to self-soothe and escape from your current distress.

Unfortunately, consuming unhealthy foods to feel better in the short term exacerbates negative emotions in the long term.

Junk foods and processed foods have been shown to harm our emotions and mood.[2] These foods are often high in refined carbohydrates, sugar, and unhealthy fats, which can lead to a rapid spike and subsequent drop in blood sugar levels. This can cause feelings of fatigue, irritability, and mood swings. Additionally, regularly consuming these foods can lead to chronic inflammation in the body, which has been linked to an increased risk of depression and anxiety.[3]

Additionally, junk foods and processed foods are often high in additives and preservatives that can negatively affect your brain chemistry. For example, some artificial sweeteners have been linked to changes in brain activity that can lead to increased hunger and overeating.[4] Further, some food additives and preservatives have been shown to disrupt the balance of neurotransmitters in the brain, leading to mood disturbances and other emotional imbalances.

So, by eating to soothe your feelings, you are, in turn, making those emotions worse. You are now caught in a harmful emotional eating cycle.

The Emotional Eating Cycle

It's NOT All About Willpower

In my own healing journey, one of the things that truly put me down was when people said that I should *"get over it," "move on,"* or *"just commit."* I felt bad after each unsupportive comment. This would, of course, send me into another emotional eating frenzy. After which, I would spend every free thought beating myself up for my food choices and how I looked and felt.

Many people looked at me and thought I was weak and lacked willpower. Deep inside, I did not believe this. For one, I knew my co-morbid mental health issues hampered me. Second, I did well in school and was determined to finish high school with the best grades possible so I could go to a good college. So, I thought to myself, *"If I have that determination and am willing to do what it takes to achieve it, I do have willpower!"*

So, why did I not have the same willpower regarding food? It's because **emotional eating is more than just willpower**.

As kids, most of us are taught to use food to make ourselves feel better. So, as adults, we eat when we are sad and want to feel better, not because we are hungry. So, emotional eating is a very strong learned behavior.[5]

Additionally, these "reward foods" or "pleasure foods" we were given as children were usually high in sugar and fat (e.g., candy, ice cream, cake, donuts, etc.). According to research, eating high-fat, high-calorie, and high-sugar foods changes the brain's reward centers.[6,7] We have trained our brains to react more positively when we eat the "bad stuff" than the "good stuff."

Research has also shown that emotional eating is a behavior that may become more linked to the trigger than the relief itself.[8] For example, if you reach for a bag of Doritos each time you are stressed, you are most likely to eat it because that is what your brain has been conditioned to do. That is, reaching for chips and eating them is an automatic habit linked to stress, not to any relief that may result from eating them.

The above situations have nothing to do with willpower. So, willpower alone is insufficient to overcome the underlying emotional triggers and habits that lead to emotional eating. What you need to do is to *replace* this coping mechanism. You need to learn new ways to deal with your emotions.

In Chapter 2: Dialectical Behavior Therapy 101, you will learn all these new ways. And here is the best part: as you discover healthier ways to deal with unpleasant emotions, your "willpower" will naturally grow. But first, let us learn what causes emotional eating.

Emotional Eating: Causes and Triggers

Emotional eating is a complex behavior that various factors can cause. Still, understanding its possible causes is important in developing effective strategies to manage your emotional eating and develop a healthy relationship with food.

Emotional eating can have various underlying causes, including the following:

1) **Stress**. When stressed, the body releases the hormone *cortisol*, which increases appetite and cravings for high-calorie foods. Additionally, stress can trigger negative emotions, leading to emotional eating to cope with these feelings.[9,10,11]

2) **Trauma**. Individuals who have experienced trauma, such as physical, emotional, or sexual abuse, may turn to food to cope with their emotional pain.[12,13] Additionally, trauma can alter the brain's reward system, making individuals more likely to seek high-calorie foods to regulate emotions.

3) **Low self-esteem**. Individuals with low self-esteem may use food to cope with negative emotions or seek comfort and pleasure. Although food may temporarily relieve negative feelings, it can also reinforce a negative self-image. Furthermore, chronic emotional eating can lead to weight gain,

further damaging self-esteem and perpetuating the cycle of emotional eating.[14,15,16]

4) **Depression and anxiety**. Individuals with depression or anxiety may use food as a coping mechanism to deal with negative emotions, stress or overwhelm, or seek comfort and pleasure. Emotional eating can temporarily relieve these negative feelings. Still, it can reinforce guilt or shame and lead to other negative emotions.[17,18,19]

5) **Boredom**. People may eat when bored to distract themselves from their boredom or to add excitement to their day. Eating can also serve as a way to pass the time or fill a void.[20,21]

6) **Social and cultural factors**. Social norms, family customs, peer pressure, and cultural beliefs can all influence your relationship with food and eating habits.[22,23] For example, social gatherings that involve food may encourage overeating or consuming unhealthy foods. Cultural beliefs that promote the "clean your plate" mentality can also contribute to emotional eating.[24] (See also The Clean Your Plate Syndrome, page 148.)

7) **Dieting history**. When you follow a strict diet plan to lose weight, you may become obsessed with food, leading to feelings of deprivation and intense cravings. This can result in binge eating episodes, becoming a habit and a coping mechanism for dealing with negative emotions. Dieting can also disrupt the body's hunger and fullness cues, making distinguishing between emotional and physical hunger harder.[25,26]

8) **Genetics**. Some evidence suggests that genetics may play a role in emotional eating. Studies have shown that certain genes can affect a person's appetite, cravings, and response to stress and emotions.[27,28]

Impact of Emotional Eating on Your Mental and Physical Health

Mental Health

Emotional eating can greatly affect your mental health. When you use food to cope with your emotions, it can lead to feelings of guilt, shame, and regret. It can also lead to a disconnection from your emotions. You may find it difficult to identify and process your feelings if you use food to suppress or avoid uncomfortable emotions. This can ultimately lead to a sense of numbness or emotional exhaustion.

Although emotional eating is not a disorder, it can be a symptom of a mental health disorder. For instance, someone with Major Depressive Disorder (MDD) may turn to food to cope with their depression. In contrast, someone with General Anxiety Disorder (GAD) may use food to calm their nerves or distract themselves from their worries.

People with Post-Traumatic Stress Disorder (PTSD) may use food to cope with trauma-related emotions and memories. At the same time, those with Borderline Personality Disorder (BPD) may turn to food to regulate their moods or deal with feelings of emptiness. Emotional eating can also be a sign of binge eating disorder, in which people repeatedly eat large amounts of food, often in secret and while feeling out of control.

Important: Emotional eating alone does not mean you have a mental health disorder. However, when it becomes a persistent pattern of behavior and begins to impact your quality of life, it may be a sign of an underlying issue that needs to be addressed.

Physical Health

Emotional hunger cannot be satisfied with food. As such, you tend to want to it more and more, which can lead to negative impacts on your physical health, such as the following:

1. **Weight gain**. Emotional eaters usually consume more food than they need. These foods are also often high-calorie, high-fat, and high-sugar. As such, weight gain and obesity are common side effects. Additionally, emotional eating often involves mindless eating, where you do not pay attention to portion sizes or fullness cues, leading to overeating. Emotional eating can also disrupt normal hunger and satiety signals, leading to a cycle of eating whether you are hungry or not. Over time, emotional eating can contribute to weight gain and difficulty maintaining a healthy weight.

2. **Poor digestion**. Mindless eating usually means not chewing your food properly, leading to larger particles that are more difficult to digest. The stress hormones released during emotional eating, such as cortisol, can also disrupt digestion by slowing the digestive process and reducing the production of digestive enzymes. The unhealthy foods consumed can also lead to gut inflammation, causing digestive issues such as bloating, gas, constipation, and diarrhea.

3. **Fatigue**. Unhealthy foods can cause a sudden spike in blood sugar, followed almost immediately by a crash. This drastic up and down of your blood sugar levels can lead to feelings of fatigue and lethargy. Additionally,

emotional eating can disrupt sleep patterns, which can also contribute to feelings of fatigue. For example, if you eat a large amount of food or eat late at night, your body is still working to digest the food while trying to sleep, leading to less restful sleep.

Emotional eating can also lead to "emotional fatigue." Feelings of guilt, shame, and regret associated with emotional eating can lead to another bout of emotional eating. This roller coaster of negative feelings-eating to feeling better-negative feelings can leave you emotionally exhausted.

4. **Skin problems**. Eating a diet high in sugar and processed foods can cause inflammation and lead to skin problems such as acne, eczema, and premature aging. The resulting fatigue and low-quality sleep from emotional eating can also affect skin health and contribute to dark circles and puffiness under the eyes. Further, any resulting weight gain can stretch the skin and cause stretch marks.

5. **Insomnia**. When you eat large amounts of food, particularly sugary or high-fat foods, your body must work harder to digest them. This can cause discomfort, bloating, and indigestion, making falling or staying asleep difficult. Additionally, emotional eating can cause a surge of energy, making it harder to feel tired and ready for sleep.

6. **Increased risk of chronic diseases**. Consistently engaging in emotional eating can increase the risk of developing chronic diseases such as high blood pressure, high cholesterol levels, diabetes, heart disease, stroke, and certain types of cancer.

7. **Nutrient deficiencies**. Eating processed and unhealthy foods can lead to nutrient deficiencies, as these foods often lack essential vitamins and

minerals for optimal health. Emotional eating may also disrupt the body's ability to absorb and utilize nutrients, further exacerbating the problem of nutrient deficiencies.

8. **Weakened immune system.** An unhealthy diet can weaken the immune system, making you prone to various infections and illnesses such as colds, flus, and pneumonia.

9. **Increased inflammation.** Eating processed and high-fat foods can cause inflammation in the body, increasing the risk of several chronic diseases such as arthritis, asthma, diabetes, and even Alzheimer's disease[29].

10. **Poor physical performance.** A diet high in processed foods and sugar can lead to poor physical performance, affecting your fitness levels. These foods can make you feel sluggish, bloated, and tired, making engaging in physical activities like exercise or even simple daily tasks harder. Additional weight gained from emotional eating can further reduce physical performance by putting more strain on your joints and muscles.

Emotional eating can have serious, damaging consequences on your physical and mental health. This coping mechanism may provide short-term relief, but it is actually causing long-term damage to your mind and body.

To live the life you deserve, you must develop healthier coping mechanisms for unpleasant emotions. The next chapters will assist you in doing so.

Chapter 2: Dialectical Behavior Therapy 101

"Healing is about breaking the cycle of bad habits and patterns."— Unknown

What is DBT?

Dialectical Behavior Therapy, or DBT, is a type of therapy that helps people learn new ways of managing intense emotions and improving relationships with others. It was developed in the 1980s by Dr. Marsha M. Linehan[30] due to her and her colleagues' work with individuals suffering from Borderline Personality Disorder (BPD). Today, however, DBT treats various conditions, such as depression, anxiety, and eating disorders.

DBT is a form of CBT. However, while CBT focuses on identifying and converting negative thought patterns into positive ones (change-focused), DBT applies two opposing (dialectical) tactics: **Acceptance** and **Change**.

How DBT Can Be Used to Treat Emotional Eating

DBT was primarily developed for people suffering from BPD, which involves *difficulty regulating emotions* as one of its primary symptoms. Emotional eating is the propensity to use food in response to positive or negative emotions. As such, DBT is a great technique to address the issues associated with emotional eating and other eating problems.[31,32,33]

DBT Primary Concepts: Acceptance and Change

Dr. Linehan states that when she first started to work with individuals with BPD, she applied traditional behavior therapy techniques, which were change-focused. Clients would then question this method and say something like, *"What?! You mean I am the problem?"*

This prompted Dr. Linehan to change tactics and use acceptance strategies. She would listen to patients and urge them to be open and accepting of their feelings and experiences. However, these prompted clients to say, *"You mean you are not going to help me?"*

At this point, Dr. Linehan realized that she needed to find a way to bring acceptance and change strategies together. Fortunately, she was able to do so, resulting in a new type of therapy called DBT.

Radical Acceptance

Acceptance is reality acceptance in DBT. You are encouraged to accept your current reality AS IS. There is no need to question, evaluate or judge your past or the circumstances leading you to emotional eating. You cannot change what has happened, so spending time on it is futile.

This may appear simple or easy, but as someone who has struggled with mental health issues and emotional eating for many years, I am the first to say it is not.

When you experience emotional pain, your brain interprets it as threatening your well-being. Your natural response is to try to ignore, avoid or escape it. However, when you cannot immediately escape the source of the pain, your brain is likely to continue to focus on it, analyzing and meditating on the experience in an attempt to find a solution or relief. So you either try to avoid the emotional pain or focus on it. Either way, you are prolonging your suffering because neither avoiding the problem nor ruminating on it fixes it.

So the first step to moving on involves accepting your reality rather than fighting against it or trying to change it. It means acknowledging and accepting the present moment, even if it is painful or difficult, rather than trying to deny or escape it. Acceptance must also be complete, not just lip service. You must accept with your whole heart, mind, and body. In DBT, this is called **Radical Acceptance**.

Worksheet: Radical Acceptance

Radical Acceptance is a freeing concept; it involves nothing but accepting your current reality. There is no need to assess, question, or judge anything; there is also no room for doubt, blame, or fear. Just acceptance.

Inside the circle, write down your thoughts about your current reality. There are no right or wrong answers. Just write whatever comes to mind.

Examples: (1) I accept that I use food to cope with my emotions. (2) I accept that my emotional eating has led to weight gain and health problems. (3) I eat when I am lonely. (4) I eat when I am bored. (5) I do not know why I eat even when I am not hungry.

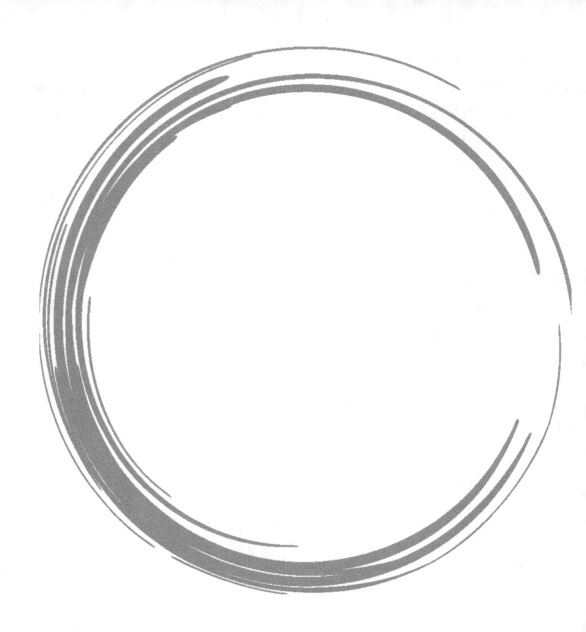

Desire to Change

If Radical Acceptance is half of the equation, **Change** is the other half. Why? Because whatever it is you are doing is not working for you. Continuing down the road of emotional eating is not in your best interest. But the good news is there are *other* roads to take, and you just need to discover them.

Change is not easy, and that is true. The human brain does not like change[34]. One of the primary reasons is that humans are creatures of habit and routine, and change disrupts our established patterns and comfort zones. Additionally, change often involves uncertainty and unpredictability, which can be uncomfortable. We also have a natural aversion to risk and loss, making change seem daunting and intimidating. Lastly, change is often seen as a "problem" or "challenge" instead of a chance to learn, grow, and improve. However, as American entrepreneur, author, and motivational speaker Jim Rohn said, *"Your life doesn't get better by chance. It gets better by change."*

So if you want to live healthier and be happier, change is what you need to do. You can only break the chains of emotional eating by learning new habits and skills.

Worksheet: Desire to Change

This exercise will assist you in welcoming change in your life. There is no need to make any plans here. Just write down your thoughts about change in the circle below. Remember, there are no right or wrong answers. Just write whatever comes to mind.

Examples: (1) I am willing to learn new ways to manage my feelings. (2) I am ready for "better." (3) I am willing to make positive changes. (4) I am ready to stop using food to numb my pain. (5) I am ready to stop using food to feel loved.

Worksheet: Radical Acceptance + Desire to Change

It is time to bring Radical Acceptance and Desire to Change together.

RADICAL ACCEPTANCE: Write statements accepting your current situation.

DESIRE TO CHANGE: Write statements expressing your desire to change or how change can benefit your life.

DECLARATION: Be kind to yourself as you acknowledge today and your wants and needs for tomorrow.

RADICAL ACCEPTANCE:	DECLARATION:	DESIRE TO CHANGE:
I accept that I use food to cope with my emotions.	*"I accept who I am today. I am tired of fighting myself, and others. Life is full of ups and downs, and I can't control everything. So I've decided not to struggle against things I can't change.*	*I am willing to learn new ways to manage my feelings.*
I eat when I am lonely.		*I'm ready for "better."*
I accept that my emotional eating has led to weight gain and health problems.	*I may not have caused all my problems but I accept that I have to solve them anyway—for my own benefit.*	*I am willing to make positive changes.*
I eat when I am bored.		*I am ready to stop using food to numb my pain.*
I do not know why I eat even when I am not hungry.	*I also accept that I'm not living my best life now. So I am opening that door to change. I am going to give myself the opportunity to be "better." I deserve it.*	*I am ready to stop using food to feel loved.*

DBT Primary Skills: Mindfulness, Distress Tolerance, Emotion Regulation, Interpersonal Effectiveness

In addition to the application of dialectics (Acceptance + Change), DBT is also unique because it is skill-based therapy. As Dr. Linehan says, *"DBT uses skills intentionally and wisely. Everyone who comes into DBT gets skills."*

At the time, most traditional therapies were focused on *behavioral change*. However, the HOW is often missing. For example, emotional eaters are often encouraged to practice "mindful eating," but how exactly do you do that? What are the steps?

Dr. Linehan ensured that people who took her program developed new skills that produced the desired behavioral change. And this change of behavior will then produce the outcomes you want out of life.

DBT SKILLS -> BEHAVIORAL CHANGE -> DESIRED OUTCOME IN LIFE

In DBT, the four primary skills to master are Mindfulness, Distress Tolerance, Emotion Regulation, and Interpersonal Effectiveness.

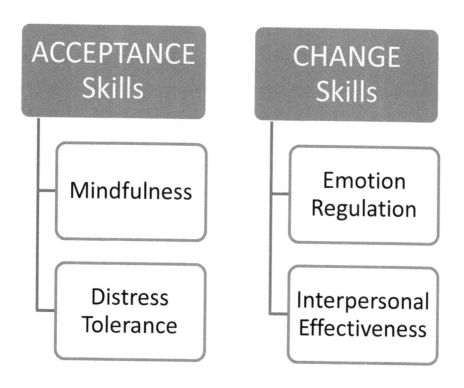

As you can see in the figure above, Acceptance is achieved by learning Mindfulness and Distress Tolerance skills. At the same time, Change is realized by learning Emotion Regulation and Interpersonal Effectiveness skills.

The succeeding chapters will explain each DBT skill in detail. Numerous exercises will be provided for each skill. Why? Because learning involves both knowing and doing.

Reading and understanding DBT skills is one thing, but to genuinely effect positive change in your life, you must practice these skills in real-world settings. In short, learning entails obtaining theoretical knowledge AND putting that knowledge into practice! The exercises provided are how you will accomplish this.

Important: The exercises are NOT intended to be one-time activities. I encourage you to apply what you learn in your daily life regularly. To be honest, this is actually easier than you think.

For example, remember when you first learned how to ride a bicycle? You had to practice balancing, pedaling, steering, and maybe even memorize biking regulations in your area. However, over time and with consistent practice, you simply... biked. Today, you do not even think about many things when you ride your bike; you just do it. Remember this as you learn the DBT skills in the next pages. They may be "new" today, but over time, and with consistent application, they will become second nature to you.

Chapter 3: Mindfulness Skills for Emotional Eating

"Mindfulness can help people of any age reshape their relationship with food and eating."— Dr. Susan Albers

---

Introduction to Mindfulness

Mindfulness is the practice of paying attention to the present moment without judgment. It involves being aware of your thoughts, feelings, and surroundings and accepting them without trying to change or resist them. Practicing mindfulness teaches you to be more present, focused, and calm.

Why is mindfulness important? In many ways, emotional eating is a knee-jerk reaction to emotions. Emotional eaters reach for food out of habit and often do not take the time to think about the consequences of this habit. Mindfulness helps improve your mental control. With this skill, you will learn to become more aware of your emotions rather than reacting to them with food.

For starters, let us begin your mindfulness practice by using your breath. Just like eating, breathing is so basic, so mundane, no? So much so that you do not really think about how you are breathing. For example, have you ever thought of how short or long you take each breath? Have you ever noticed how your breath reacts to a specific event, place, or person?

Also, did you know that most people are shallow breathers? These are fast and short breaths that only fill a tiny area of the lungs. Shallow breathing does not stimulate mindfulness. So, let us begin your mindfulness practice by learning how to breathe deeper and with more intention.

Worksheet: Belly Breathing

Belly breathing, or diaphragmatic breathing, aids in relaxation and stress relief. It's an excellent first-time workout for shallow breathers. The steps for belly breathing are as follows.

1. Take a seat or lie down on your bed.
2. Place one hand on your tummy and one on your chest.
3. Gently inhale through your nose, allowing your stomach to expand like a balloon. (Your chest should be quite motionless.)
4. Slowly exhale through your lips, allowing your belly to shrink like a balloon. (Try to expel all of the air from your lungs.)
5. Continue to breathe in this manner, focusing on the sensation of your abdomen rising and falling with each breath, like gentle ocean waves.

Ensure you breathe deeply from your diaphragm, not shallowly from your chest. You can also use this technique with your eyes closed, envisioning a peaceful landscape to help you relax. As you become more familiar with this method, gradually lengthen your belly breaths.

Worksheet: Take 5

This five-minute breathing exercise gives your mind and body time to relax.

1. Set a timer for five minutes.
2. Find a comfortable and quiet place where you will not be interrupted.
3. Take a seat or lie down on your bed.
4. Close your eyes and take a deep breath through your nose, counting to five as you inhale.
5. Hold your breath for a count of five.
6. Slowly exhale through your mouth, counting to five as you release your breath.
7. Repeat this process until the timer sounds.

Notes:

- As you do the above exercise, focus on the sensation of air moving in and out of your body, and let go of any distracting thoughts.
- When you are finished, take a moment to notice how you feel, and then slowly open your eyes.

Worksheet: 4-7-8 Breathing

4-7-8 Breathing is an advanced breathing technique that encourages deep relaxation. In this workout, you will exhale and hold your breath for longer than you inhale.

1. Find a comfortable and quiet place where you will not be interrupted.
2. Take a seat or lie down on your bed.
3. Close your eyes and take a few deep breaths to relax your body.
4. INHALE for 4 counts through your nose.

5. HOLD YOUR BREATH for 7 counts...

6. EXHALE for 8 counts through your mouth.

7. Do steps 4-6 for at least four cycles.

Mindful Eating

Mindful eating is being present at the moment and paying attention to the experience of eating without judgment or distraction. It is to develop a healthier relationship with food and to become more attuned to your body's needs and signals.

Principles of Mindful Eating

Here are some of the principles of mindful eating:

1. **Engage all of your senses while eating.** When you eat, interact with the food with all your senses. For example, use your eyes to notice the colors of food, your nose to register its smells, your tongue to notice the textures and tastes of the food, etc.

2. **Eat slowly and savor your food**. When you eat slowly, you give yourself time to fully taste and enjoy your food, increasing your satisfaction and making you less likely to overeat.

3. **Pay attention to your hunger and fullness cues.** Mindful eating is also observing your hunger and fullness cues. For example, is your stomach growling? If so, you may still be hungry. However, if you feel a sense of fullness or pressure in your stomach, that is a fullness cue, and you should stop eating.

   It is believed that it takes about 20 to 30 minutes for your brain to receive fullness signals from your stomach. So, you may think you are still hungry, but you already have enough. This is also why eating slowly (tip #2 above) is important. In short, do not rush your meals. Give your body time to tell you that you are full.

4. **Notice and acknowledge the thoughts and emotions that arise while eating.** Taking note of what you are thinking and feeling during a meal is important. It encourages you to be aware of your internal experiences and how they may affect your eating behavior. For instance, when you reach for and eat cookies in front of the TV, ask yourself, "*Why did I do that when I just had dinner,* " or "*Why do I want cookies now?*" This will help you identify why you use food as a coping mechanism.

5. **Cultivate a non-judgmental attitude towards your eating habits.** Mindful eating involves noticing and observing your thoughts and emotions around food without judging or criticizing yourself. For example, if you notice that you reach for cookies each time you are bored, there is no need to feel ashamed, guilty, or judge yourself. Radically accept what you have done and your reason(s) for it, and work on learning new ways to change.

6. **Make conscious and intentional food choices.** Remember that food is meant to *nourish* your body. As a result, choose foods that keep your body healthy and performing at its best rather than unhealthy foods that negatively affect your mood and make your body sick.

7. **Practice gratitude and appreciation for the food you eat.** We often forget to be thankful for what we eat. However, expressing appreciation can help you build a more positive relationship with food and make you attentive to the nourishing advantages of the food you eat. Additionally, practicing gratitude during meals will help you slow down and taste your food more.

In Japan, saying thanks before and after a meal is a habit. They say *Itadakimasu*, which means *Let us eat* or *Bon Appétit*, then at the end of the meal, they say *Gochisosama*, which means they are grateful for the sumptuous meal they just had. These words demonstrate the Japanese enthusiasm for not only the food itself but also for all that went into putting the meal in front of them.

8. **Be mindful of the environmental and social impact of your food choices.** You are not living alone on this planet; your food choices affect your family, friends, the environment, the community, and the world. This principle encourages you to choose healthy foods for yourself, others, and the planet, such as locally sourced and sustainably grown produce, grass-fed meat, and wild-caught fish.

Benefits of Mindful Eating

Mindful eating is not just a way to develop a healthier relationship with food and to prevent using food as a coping mechanism. Here are some of its other benefits.

1. **Helps with weight management.** Mindful eating can help you regulate your eating habits, increasing awareness of hunger and fullness cues. It can also reduce overeating, which can aid in weight management.[35,36]

2. **Improves digestion.** Eating slowly and mindfully helps your body digest food more effectively and reduces digestive discomfort.

3. **Reduces stress**. Mindful eating encourages relaxation and helps you become more aware of your body, reducing stress and promoting a sense of well-being.

4. **Increases enjoyment of food.** By savoring each bite and fully experiencing the taste, texture, and smell of your food, you can increase your enjoyment of meals and find greater satisfaction in eating.

5. **Promotes healthier food choices.** Mindful eating can help you become more aware of the impact of your food choices on your emotions, body, and the environment. As such, it will encourage you to choose healthier, more nutritious foods.

6. **Enhances mindful awareness.** Mindful eating can enhance your overall mindfulness practice by increasing awareness of your thoughts, emotions, and physical sensations during eating.

7. **Improves overall health.** By reducing stress, improving digestion, promoting healthier food choices, and enhancing mindful awareness, mindful eating can contribute to overall health and well-being. For instance, research shows better food choices and intake may lead to better sleep.[37,38]

Now that you understand how mindful eating can help you avoid emotional eating, try some of the mindful eating exercises on the following pages.

Worksheet: Mindful Eating

1. If you have time, do the <u>**Take 5**</u> breathing exercise (page 39). It will destress your nervous system and improve your digestion and metabolism.

2. **Choose a food item.** Select a food item you want to eat mindfully, such as fruit or a small snack.

What food item did you choose?

Example: tangerine, lunch salad, etc.

_____

_____

_____

_____

3. **Settle in.** Sit down at a table or in a quiet place to focus on your food without distractions.

4. **Observe and engage all your senses.** Take a moment to observe the food in front of you. Use all of your senses as you interact with the food.

What do you see?

Example: the dark orange color of my tangerine

_____

_____

_____

_____

What sounds do you associate with this food?

Example: a soft ripping sound as I peel the tangerine

_____

_____

_____

_____

What do you smell?

Example: the distinct citrusy smell of tangerines

_____

_____

_____

_____

What is the texture of the food?

Example: the tangerine is firm but soft

_____

_____

_____

_____

What does your food taste like?

Example: the tangerine is very sweet

_____

_____

_____

_____

5. **Take small bites**. Take a small bite of the food and chew it slowly, paying attention to its taste and texture.

6. **Pause**. Put down the food and take a deep breath. Notice how the food feels in your mouth and how your body responds to it.

7. **Repeat**. Repeat steps 5 and 6 until you have finished the food item.

8. **Reflect**. Take a moment to reflect on the experience.

How did it feel to eat mindfully?

Example: It was weird at first. I didn't realize I was eating so fast before. The first time I tried this, it felt like I was eating forever.

_____

_____

_____

_____

What did you notice about the food?

Example: Now that I was taking time to eat the tangerine, I realized there were so many "steps" before I put the fruit in my mouth. I never really thought about those steps before.

_____

_____

_____

_____

How did you feel using all your senses while eating?

Example: It felt like I was "tasting" the food more!

_____

_____

_____

_____

Worksheet: TASTE

TASTE[39] is a great technique to remember when trying to eat mindfully.

T	**T**hink Before you reach out for food and put anything in your mouth, take a moment to think if you want food due to physical hunger or because you are reacting to emotion.
A	**A**ppreciate Take the time to think about what happened before the food was brought to you. Think about how much energy and resources went into making your meal.
S	Eat **S**lowly Eat slowly. Chew multiple times until the food is properly broken down before you swallow. Doing this will improve digestion and give your stomach enough time to signal to your brain that you are reaching satiety. **Tip**: Put down your fork between bites to force yourself to eat slower.
T	Take the **T**ime to enjoy your meal As you chew, take the time to enjoy the flavors of the meal in your mouth. **Tip**: See if you can tell which flavor comes from which ingredient!
E	**E**nd your meal when satisfied Finish eating when you feel satisfied, not when you are stuffed. You will derive more pleasure from your meal this way.

Worksheet: Wise Mind

Wise Mind is our inner wisdom. It is the union of our emotional and rational selves. Emotional eaters usually let their emotions take complete control of the situation. Emotion prompts eating; ergo, we eat.

However, as you know, emotional eating brings in a lot of feelings of guilt, shame, and remorse. So you should not let your emotions rule. On the other hand, making decisions or taking actions based 100% on logic is also not a good idea. This is because it implies ignoring the feelings *behind* your emotional eating.

My sadness and the fact that I felt very alone at school led to my emotional eating. (At this point, I was listening to my Emotional Mind.) If I had just stopped eating junk food because I was gaining weight, I would have been using my Reasonable Mind, but I wouldn't have understood that I was eating to avoid being alone. I wouldn't have realized that food was a self-soothing strategy substituting for friends.

So, the best way to proceed is to learn to consult Emotional Mind and Rational Mind (to enter Wise Mind).

EMOTIONAL MIND:

loneliness

boredom

sadness

anger

acting 100% on my emotions

guilt

shame

reactive or defensive

WISE MIND

Wise Mind is the middle ground between feeling and thinking.

It takes feelings into account, but it also thinks about what makes sense before moving or reacting.

REASONABLE MIND:

facts

statistics

data

acting 100% using reason

focused

organized

non-judgmental

Now, it is your turn to practice Wise Mind.

1. Think about the last time you emotionally ate.

2. Under **Emotional Mind**, please write down how you felt or your mood when you started thinking about food.

   Example: *I was feeling sad and lonely.*

3. Under **Reasonable Mind**, write down facts about the situation. (What do you KNOW for sure?)

Example: *I just had dinner. I should not have been thinking or wanting food.*

4. Under **Wise Mind,** write down any conclusions you reach after combining emotions and logic.

   Example: *I am feeling sad and lonely right now. That is okay; my feelings are valid. But I know I do not need to eat right now. I am not physically hungry. So I'll call my best friend and chat for a few mins.*

EMOTIONAL MIND　　　　　　**REASONABLE MIND**

WISE MIND

Chapter 4: Distress Tolerance Skills for Emotional Eating

"The more you tolerate, the more you can change."
— Dr. Marsha Linehan

Introduction to Distress Tolerance

Distress tolerance is crisis survival. In terms of emotional eating, distress tolerance is your ability to withstand your cravings or urge to reach for food in response to emotions.

Stress and Emotional Eating

Stress and emotional eating are closely related.[40,41] Many people use food to cope with stress, anxiety, and other negative emotions. When we experience stress, our bodies release hormones like *cortisol* and *adrenaline*, increasing our appetite and cravings for high-calorie, high-fat foods.

Unfortunately, the relationship between stress and emotional eating can become a vicious cycle. Emotional eating can lead to weight gain and other health problems, which can cause additional stress and negative emotions. This can lead to further emotional eating, creating a cycle of negative thoughts, emotions, and behaviors.

Stress vs. Distress

Stress is a typical reaction to the demands and pressures of everyday life. It can be positive or negative, motivating us to take action and perform well.

Positive stress, also known as *eustress*, can enhance our performance, increase our focus and alertness, and help us achieve our goals. For example, say you are preparing to give a presentation at work. Eustress can drive you to be more focused and to work harder to ensure a successful presentation.

Distress is a negative form of stress that can lead to physical, emotional, and psychological problems. Distress is often the result of chronic or overwhelming stress that is not managed effectively. For example, say you are preparing to give a presentation at work. Distress can make you chaotic, procrastinate and turn to emotional eating.

Importance of Distress Tolerance Skills for Emotional Eating

It is not only stress that may prompt a person to eat emotionally. Practically ANY emotion can trigger emotional eating because, as mentioned before, but emotional eating can also be a reaction to both negative (loneliness, sadness, boredom, etc.) and positive emotions (a.k.a. happy eating[42]).

As such, distress tolerance skills are not just about tolerating or surviving stress per se. It is about giving you the tools so that you DO NOT reach for food due to your emotions, whether positive or negative.

Here are some of the potential benefits of increasing your distress tolerance:

1. **Eliminates or reduces emotional eating**. Distress tolerance skills can help you tolerate and manage your emotions without resorting to food. This can reduce the frequency and intensity of emotional eating episodes or eliminate them altogether.

2. **Improves emotional regulation.** Developing distress tolerance skills can help you better manage and regulate your emotions, reducing the likelihood of emotional eating in the future.

3. **Increases resilience**. Increasing distress tolerance, levels can help you become more resilient in the face of stress and adversity. You may feel more confident handling difficult situations without relying on food as a coping mechanism.

4. **Enhances problem-solving skills**. As you become better at managing distress (i.e., your need to reach out for food), you will develop stronger problem-solving skills and become more adept at finding solutions to the underlying issues causing your emotional eating.

5. **Improved overall well-being**. Developing distress tolerance skills can help reduce stress, improve your emotional well-being, and enhance your overall quality of life.

Let us now work on increasing your distress tolerance using the exercises below.

Worksheet: Self-Soothe Using Your Five Senses

Grounding strategies bring you back to the present moment, giving you time to disconnect from your desire to reach for food. You will use your five senses—sight, smell, sound, touch, and taste—for this grounding practice to help you stay centered and focused and reduce feelings of (emotional) hunger.

List FIVE (5) things you can see right now.

Example: water bottle, fern plant, pear tree outside, neighbor's window, post-it notes

1.

2.

3.

4.

5.

List FOUR (4) things you can touch right now.

Example: my sweater, keyboard, mouse, PC monitor

1.

2.

3.

4.

List THREE (3) things you can hear right now.

Example: birds chirping, passing cars, co-workers typing on their keyboard

1.

2.

3.

List TWO (2) things you can smell right now.

Example: office room deodorizer, my hand lotion

1.

2.

List ONE (1) thing you can taste right now.

Example: coffee

1.

If you are still thinking of food after this exercise, do this practice again or write down as many things as possible per sense.

Worksheet: The Grounding Grid

Choose an activity from the **Grounding Grid** below whenever you feel the need to eat in response to your feelings. I have jumpstarted the list per grid to give you ideas. Please feel free to add more to the list.

THE GROUNDING GRID	
What do you want to do?	
SELF-CARE	**PHYSICAL ACTIVITY**
1. Relaxing bath	1. Walk outside
2. Massage	2. 5- minute stretch
3. 15-minute digital break	3. Climb up and down the stairs
4.	4.
5.	5.
6.	6.
7.	7.
CREATIVE PURSUITS	**MINDFULNESS**
1. Painting	1. Belly breathing (38)
2. Drawing	2. Take 5 (page 39)
3. Writing	3. 10-minute quiet meditation
4.	4.
5.	5.
6.	6.
7.	7.
SOCIAL CONNECTION	
1. Call a family member	
2. Message a friend	
3. Go over to a colleague and invite them to a quick break	
4.	

5.

6.

7.

Worksheet: STOP

STOP is another great exercise to keep yourself from acting impulsively based on your emotions.

S	**Stop** Stop in your tracks! Literally, freeze in place and be motionless. Imagine a big STOP sign right in front of you. Stopping physically prevents you from doing what your emotions urge you to do. For example, suppose you are a boredom grazer and have a habit of going to the kitchen to find something to nibble on when bored. In this case, physically freeze, stay in place, and imagine the kitchen as "closed."
T	**Take a step back** When emotional hunger strikes, "thinking straight" can be difficult. So, give yourself time to process by mentally or even physically stepping back. Here is an example of mentally stepping back: close your eyes and take deep breaths until you feel the urge slipping away. Here is an example of physically stepping back: suppose you are at a party with many unhealthy snacks and drinks. However, you just had a meal. In this situation, physically step out of the room.

Observe

Pay attention to what is going on inside and outside of you. Take notes as if you were making a list. Observing distracts your attention from your urges by occupying your mind with something else.

Examples of self-observation:
I am standing between a door and a weird-looking chair.
As I look down, I notice that my shoes need dusting.

What are you observing about yourself? (List down as many as you can.)

_____

_____

_____

_____

_____

_____

Examples of observing your environment:
Mom's plants need watering.
Dad is somewhere in the garden.

What are you observing about your environment?

_____

_____

_____

_____

_____

_____

O

Proceed mindfully

Kudos! You have distracted yourself successfully. Now it is time to move on—mindfully. You do not want to be in the same emotional situation, so ensure you move forward in the right direction. Ask yourself questions like, "What is the best course of action to do right now?" or "What can I do to prevent myself form being in this situation?

What is the best course of action to do right now?

Example: (1) Get up from the sofa. (2) Brush my teeth. (3) Go to bed.

_____

_____

_____

What can I do to prevent myself from being in this situation?

Example: Remove all the "nibbles" I have in front of the TV.

_____

_____

_____

P

Worksheet: TIPP

Did you know you can change how you feel by changing your body chemistry?[43] The **TIPP** techniques listed below are simple to implement and work quickly to relieve you of any food thoughts.

Temperature

Emotions occur in the body. Rapidly changing your body's temperature will help you lower the strength of your emotions.

Splash your face with cold water or wear a gel mask to feel better. This helps drop your blood pressure quickly, which aids in lowering the intensity of your feelings.

Other ideas: pour cold water on your wrists and forearms, hold ice cubes, chew ice chips, stand in front of the fridge or freezer with the door open, etc.

Even though cold temperatures have long been believed to assist in changing emotions, some people find hot temperatures work best for them. For example, a hot shower might be more soothing.

Other ideas: drink a cup of hot tea or coffee, fill a hot water bottle and hug it, rub your hands together to generate heat and place them over your eyes, etc.

See what works best for you and choose accordingly.

Intense Exercise

Divert your thoughts by subjecting your body to rigorous exercise! The intensity of your desire to emotionally eat dictates how long you should be exercising.

For example, if a sudden craving hits, perhaps a 5- or 7-minute routine is all you need. You can use apps like the _5 Minute Home Workouts_ app by Olson Applications or the 7 Minute Workout by Johnson & Johnson.

However, if you are going through very unpleasant emotions and have been battling your emotional hunger for a while, then intensely exercise for at least 20 minutes. Go for a quick jug or run, climb up and down the stairs, or use apps like FitOn to find full workouts from 5 minutes to 30+ minutes.

Paced Breathing

Slowing your inhalations and exhalations and breathing deeply from your belly will help you reduce the emotional intensity of what you are feeling. If you are new to paced breathing, do Take 5 (page 39) but omit holding your breath, just focus on inhaling and exhaling. Once you are used to this, do the exercise with the step where you hold your breath for five counts. If you are ready to progress, do 4-7-8 Breathing (page 40).

Paired Muscle Relaxation

You can combine your breathing practice above with Paired Muscle Relaxation. Slowly tense your muscles (but not so much that they cramp) as you take a deep breath. And then, as you take a deep breath out, let all that tension in your muscles go.

Chapter 5: Emotion-Regulating Skills for Emotional Eating

"It's not what you're eating, it's what's eating you."
— *Janet Greeson*

Introduction to Emotion Regulation

Emotion regulation refers to your ability to recognize and manage emotions effectively. It involves developing skills to help you identify and label your emotions, understand what triggers them, and respond to them effectively.

As mentioned, emotional eating is a maladaptive coping mechanism. The word *maladaptive* is derived from the combination of two Latin words: *malus*, which means "bad," and *adaptare*, which means "to adjust or fit." Together, they form *maladaptare*, which means "to adjust poorly." From here, the word *maladaptive* is derived to describe behaviors or responses that are ineffective or counterproductive in helping individuals cope with or adjust to their environment. (In the case of emotional eaters, it is difficult to cope with their *emotional environment*.)

Many emotional eaters know what they are doing. They know they are reaching for food not because they are hungry but because of "something else." Other people do not know, or at least do not want to accept, they are emotional eaters. A friend once said, *"Oh, I'm not an emotional eater. I'm really not. I just tend to graze excessively during moments of boredom or downtime. I don't finish a whole bag of Cheetos! Just handfuls of nuts, pretzels, cheese, and a couple spoons of peanut butter. You know..."*

The point is: emotional eaters reach for food because of their emotions. But by continually doing this, you are only making things worse for yourself (emotionally, mentally, physically, financially, etc.). What you need to do is BREAK THE CYCLE of emotional eating. How? By learning emotion regulation skills. If you increase your ability to manage your emotions better, you decrease (and potentially remove) the likelihood of emotional eating.

Practicing Self-Compassion, Self-Forgiveness, and Self-Validation

Before you go ahead and learn the skills to manage your emotions (instead of letting them manage you), let us first go over three important things: *self-compassion*, *self-forgiveness*, and *self-validation*. A lot of guilt and shame surround emotional eating. So much so that emotional eaters cannot heal because they find it difficult to practice these three concepts. But, as I have learned, these three beliefs are important for developing a healthy relationship with food… and yourself.

Self-compassion entails being kind and understanding to oneself, especially during difficulties, failure, or self-doubt. It means being gentle and supportive towards oneself rather than harshly self-critical. Self-compassion involves recognizing your suffering and offering yourself the same empathy, understanding, and support a good friend offers.

Examples:
I am doing my best, and that's all I can ask of myself.
I am not alone in my struggles. Many people go through similar experiences, and reaching out for help and support is okay.

Self-forgiveness involves letting go of self-blame and negative self-judgment after a mistake or failure. It involves acknowledging your mistakes, taking responsibility for them, and then working towards repairing any harm caused. Self-forgiveness involves releasing yourself from the burden of guilt and shame and finding a way to move forward with a sense of self-acceptance and self-worth.

Examples:

I forgive myself for my past mistakes and shortcomings.
I recognize that forgiveness is a process, and I choose to be patient and gentle with myself as I work through it.

Self-validation involves recognizing and accepting your thoughts, feelings, and experiences without seeking external validation or approval. It means acknowledging and accepting one's emotions, opinions, and experiences as valid and important, regardless of whether others agree.

Examples:

I'm doing my best to manage my emotional eating and deserve credit for my efforts.
I know that healing from emotional eating is what's best for me. I deserve understanding and respect for my choices.

Do you practice these views? If not, the following worksheets should help you.

Worksheet: Self-Compassion

1. Find a quiet and comfortable place to be alone with your thoughts. Take a few deep breaths and settle yourself by sitting or lying down in a comfortable position.

2. Close your eyes and visualize a recent situation where you felt stressed, anxious, or overwhelmed. While remembering, allow yourself to experience the emotions without judging or trying to change them.

   Example: I was very lonely last Friday. The silence was deafening in my small apartment. I ended up giving in and reaching for a tub of ice cream. Remembering it now, I feel disgusted with myself.

3. Now, imagine that you are speaking to yourself as you would to a good friend going through a similar situation. What would you say to offer support, kindness, and compassion? What words of encouragement or understanding would you offer to help your friend feel better?

   Example: It's okay; no one is perfect, so don't be so hard on yourself. Everyone finds it hard to change habits they have formed over time. Just keep going, and you'll get there.

   Your turn:

   _____

   _____

   _____

   _____

4. Repeat those words silently or out loud. Use a kind and gentle tone, and offer yourself the same support and compassion you would offer a good friend.

5. As you continue to offer yourself compassion, notice how your body feels. Do you feel more relaxed, calm, or at ease? Take a few deep breaths and let yourself fully feel the good feelings of being kind to yourself.

6. Slowly open your eyes and reflect on your experience. Use this exercise anytime to offer kindness and support or to practice cultivating self-compassion daily.

Worksheet: Self-Forgiveness

1. Find a quiet and comfortable place to be alone with your thoughts. Take a few deep breaths and sit or lie down in a comfortable position to calm down.

2. Think of a situation where you gave in to your feelings, emotionally ate, and then felt a great deal of regret. Allow yourself to fully acknowledge and feel your emotions without trying to change them or judge them. (Remember, this already happened, you cannot change it.)

   Example: I was doing so well. For nearly a month, I could stay away from emotional eating. But last week, my dog Buster died. I was devastated, and before I knew it, I finished half a box of donuts. I regret that action so much because I felt that I undid my health efforts.

3. Acknowledge that everyone makes mistakes and that you are not alone in your experience. Take a deep breath and imagine releasing any self-blame or negative self-talk you may be holding onto. Visualize releasing them like letting go of a balloon.

4. Now, offer yourself forgiveness and understanding for the situation.

   Example: I forgive myself for any mistakes that I made. I am human, and I am allowed to make mistakes. I understand that I did my best at that moment and am willing to learn and grow from this experience.

_____

_____

_____

_____

5. As you continue offering forgiveness and understanding, notice how your body feels. Do you feel lighter, more at ease, or less burdened by guilt or shame? Take a few deep breaths and fully allow yourself to experience the positive feelings of self-forgiveness.

6. When you are ready, slowly open your eyes and take a moment to reflect on your experience. Use this exercise anytime to offer yourself forgiveness or to practice cultivating self-forgiveness in your daily life. Remember, self-forgiveness is a process. Be patient and kind as you work through any difficult emotions or experiences.

Worksheet: Self-Validation

1. Begin by finding a quiet, comfortable place to sit or lie down and relax. Take a few deep breaths and become present in the moment.

2. Take a moment to reflect on the last time you emotionally ate. As you recollect what happened, allow yourself to fully experience and acknowledge the emotions that come up for you. However, do not judge or criticize yourself for feeling this way.

3. Once you have identified the emotions you are experiencing, explore the thoughts or beliefs that may be driving them. Ask questions like "What am I telling myself about this situation?" "What beliefs or assumptions do I have that might contribute to these feelings?"

    What are you telling yourself about this situation?
    Example: I don't have any willpower against food.

    _____

    _____

    _____

    _____

    What beliefs or assumptions do I have that might be contributing to these feelings?
    Example: I'm just a weak person.

    _____

    _____

    _____

    _____

4. Challenge negative or self-critical thoughts by asking yourself, "Is this thought or belief true?" "What evidence do I have to support it?" "Is there a different way to interpret this situation?"

Is this thought or belief really true?
Example: I guess...

_____

_____

_____

_____

What evidence do I have to support it?
Example: It doesn't take me long to give in to food. I feel like I don't even fight the urge to eat and eat.

_____

_____

_____

_____

Are you the same in other aspects of your life?
Example: Hmmm, not really. I'm pretty good at work and don't consider myself "weak" there.

_____

_____

_____

_____

5. Once you have challenged negative thoughts or beliefs, practice self-compassion by acknowledging your difficulties and offering yourself words of kindness and encouragement.

Examples:
I am doing the best I can.
I am worthy of love and acceptance, no matter what.
I wasn't born an emotional eater; I learned to be one. So this means I can unlearn it.

_____

_____

_____

_____

6. Finally, take a few moments to reflect on any insights or learnings that have come up during this exercise. Consider how you can apply these insights to future situations and continue to practice self-validation in your daily life.

Identifying the Emotions That Trigger Your Emotional Eating

We all have different reasons for our emotional eating. For me, it was because of the extreme isolation and loneliness I experienced in my teens. It is very hard to describe the pain I felt going through days when no one even said "Hi" to me at school. So, *loneliness* is my trigger. I have been triggered by other emotions, such as stress, boredom, and anxiety as well. But the main trigger for me is loneliness. What is yours?

Worksheet: Identifying Your Emotional Triggers

Following is a step-by-step exercise to help you identify your emotional eating triggers.

1. **Start a food journal.** Begin by recording everything you eat (e.g., when, where, what) and how you feel before, during, and after. It is important to be as specific as possible with your entries, including the time of day, location, and other relevant details.

2. **Identify patterns.** After keeping your food journal for a few days, review your entries to identify patterns or trends. Look for commonalities in the types of foods you eat, the time of day you eat them, and the emotions you experience before, during, and after eating.

   Example: After writing in my food journal for two weeks, I noticed I mindlessly snack in front of my computer while working, specifically in the afternoons.

   _____

   _____

   _____

   _____

3. **Reflect on your emotions.** Take some time to reflect on the emotions you experience throughout the day. Are there certain times of day or situations that trigger strong emotions? Are there specific emotions that you find particularly challenging to manage?

   Example: I'm not bored or stressed while working, so at first, I wasn't sure why I ate so much. Then I realized I'm not really close to any of my colleagues, so maybe that's why I eat at work—to fill that gap (lack of social connection). Also, because I over-snack in the afternoon, I don't snack too much at home. I have a very fit partner, so I think I'm hiding my snacking so I don't overeat at home. Is this shame?

_____

_____

_____

_____

_____

_____

_____

_____

4. **Identify your emotional eating triggers.** Based on the data you have gathered from your food journal and reflecting on your emotions, identify specific triggers that lead you to engage in emotional eating.

Example: I tend to emotionally eat when I am alone, like when I'm not talking to anyone at work. I also tend to emotionally eat out of shame because I don't want my partner to see me making unhealthy choices.

_____

_____

_____

_____

_____

_____

_____

5. **Develop a plan.** Once you have identified your emotional eating triggers, develop a management plan.

Example:
(1) *I'll get rid of my "snack stash" at work. (My partner doesn't know about these snacks. I grocery shop for them alone and bring them straight to work.)*
(2) *I'll invite a colleague tomorrow for a walk after lunch.*
(3) *I'll talk to my partner and ask them to help me make better choices.*

Remember, identifying emotional eating triggers is an ongoing process that takes time and practice. By developing greater self-awareness and using the tools and resources available, you can learn to manage your emotions to reduce the likelihood of emotional eating.

But what if your trigger is not an emotion but a specific person (or group of people)? People are still emotional triggers.

I have noticed that being around family members makes me tremendously nervous and anxious because of my terrible childhood and the numerous arguments I still have with them. When this happens, I sometimes feel the urge to eat until I am stuffed and cannot feel anything.

Please note I love my family and know they love me. We just do not love each other the same way, or perhaps not in the ways we want to be loved. When I realized this, I developed a plan.

(1) I would visit preferably in the afternoons, not during lunch or dinner. Chinese lunches and dinners usually involve a lot of rice and carb-heavy foods. Also, my parents would insist I eat every morsel of food (Clean Your Plate

mentality), and refusing would often lead to arguments. The fights would upset me, making me want to eat when I returned home emotionally!

(2) I would visit when I am in the right mindset. I have since learned that being "obligated" to visit on specific days (i.e., Sundays) was unhealthy. For example, if I had a deadline at work and were still required to go to my parent's house, I would arrive already short-tempered and thus emotionally eaten. But I also respect my parents, so I don't just drop by. I call ahead and ask if it is convenient for them if I visit.

(3) When a visit triggers me, and I want to emotionally eat when I get back home, I stand up, grab my gear and work out at my local club to release my emotional tension. (**Tip:** If you have a go-to move like this, always have your "gear" ready. Prepare them on weekends or during your downtime. It should always be ready for you to grab and use.)

Is a specific person(s) triggering your emotional eating? If so, who?
Example: my ultra-endurance athlete twin brother

_____

_____

_____

_____

What emotions do you normally feel when you are around them?

Example: I've always felt "less" compared to him; less successful, less healthy, etc. I laugh it off during family occasions, but it gets to me. When I get home, I would experience feelings of anger and eat.

_____

_____

_____

_____

_____

_____

_____

If you cannot avoid these people, develop a plan to manage situations when you are with them.

Example: see my 3-step plan above on how I handle being with family

_____

_____

_____

_____

_____

_____

_____

Now that you have identified your trigger(s), it is time to develop ways to regulate your emotions instead of letting them control your actions.

Worksheet: The Happiness Habit

Although negative and positive emotions can trigger emotional eating, some studies suggest that negative emotions such as stress, anxiety, loneliness, and depression are more likely to lead to emotional eating.[44,45] As such, it makes sense to increase the happiness level in your life to improve your emotional eating resilience. (Note: If you are a "happy eater," someone who emotionally eats when experiencing positive emotions, please see a list of <u>Non-Food Related Rewards</u> on page 136.)

As part of my healing journey, I found a book called *The Happiness Advantage*[46] by *Shawn Achor*. In the book, an activity helped me make it a habit to remember good things and build happy memories. By doing so, I could gradually reframe my thoughts to focus on the positives in life. I hope this activity is also beneficial to you.

Write down five (5) things that you are grateful for today.

Example: my perfectly hot cup of coffee, the sweater I'm wearing my grandma knitted, the green plants that surround me at home, the watch I have been wearing for over 10 years, the 30-minute walk in the woods I took this morning

1. _____
2. _____
3. _____
4. _____
5. _____

Important: Do this gratitude habit for at least 30 consecutive days. By doing this daily, you train yourself to switch from focusing on the negative (as most people do) to the positive.

−OR−

Write down one (1) positive event that has happened to you in the last 24 hours.

Example: the call I got from an old friend I have not heard from in a while

NEXT...

Think of an activity that makes you happy and commit to doing this for 30 consecutive days.

Joyful Activity:

_____

Example: Pilates

Commitment Statement:

I will _____ for 30 days.

Example: I will start my day with a short Pilates routine for 30 days.

ALSO...

Be Mindful of Positive Experiences

Pay full attention as you do your Joyful Activity. Do not multitask or think about what you must do *after* the activity. Do not make plans; just be.

After you have completed your chosen Joyful Activity, make a list of everything you noticed. Describe your emotions, thoughts, and physical reactions as thoroughly as possible.

Be Mindful of Positive Experiences

Example: I could not fully focus on my Pilates routine this morning. I was bothered by the construction noise outside. Still, I powered through and finished the session and do not regret it!

Looking forward to tomorrow.

_____

_____

_____

_____

_____

_____

_____

_____

Worksheet: Opposite Action

Opposite Action is exactly what it means: doing the exact opposite whenever you feel you want to emotionally eat. It is a neat "life hack" to treat emotional eating. But first, a few things:

First, **Radically Accept** (page 29) that you want to eat. (**Tip**: If you have problems accepting, consult Wise Mind, page 49.)

Second, do any of the **Distress Tolerance** exercises in this book (page 52) if you feel overwhelmed by the desire to eat.

Lastly, do your preferred **Opposite Action**.

Opposite Action is effective because it is not a delaying or avoiding tactic. Doing the opposite of what you want influences how you feel about the situation. For example, say you want to eat because you are bored. But instead of eating, you do something that eliminates boredom, such as calling a friend, walking outside and seeing and greeting other people, playing an online game with others, etc. After a while, chances are you are not bored anymore, right?

In the table below, **Column A** lists unpleasant emotions that may be the reason behind your emotional eating. **Column B** shows what you would ordinarily want to do. **Column C** lists a counter-action to what you wrote under the previous column. I have put in some examples to jumpstart ideas. Please fill out the rest of the table.

OPPOSITE ACTION

A	B	C
Emotion	**Emotional Eating Impulse**	**Opposite Action**
What you are feeling.	*What you would usually do when you feel this way.*	*Write down a counter-action.*
Boredom	*Example: get some "nibbles" from the kitchen and watch something on Netflix*	*Example: start a 1,000-piece puzzle*
Emptiness	*Example: get a tub of ice cream*	*Example: go through my photos and see a lot of happy memories with friends and family*
Guilt		
Anger		

Fear		
Sadness		
Loneliness		
Frustration		
Helplessness		
Resentment		

Feel free to add more emotions and scenarios in the extra rows below.

For some people, having ONE go-to activity works better. A colleague of mine, Max[1], turned to running. He said that whenever he felt the urge to eat emotionally, he thinks, "*Oh, it is time to get in some miles.*" When he returns, he no longer feels like eating whatever he wanted before the run. Of course, he may eat for recovery, but then he always chooses healthy food items such as nuts or a hard-boiled egg and always eats in moderation. He says, "*I don't want to undo my running! So when I return, I am truly not even in the mood for what I wanted to emotionally eat.*" And another benefit is that he has no shame, guilt, or regret after running.

One of my friends, Linda[1], shared with me this great hack: "*I have multiple subscriptions to health and fitness magazines. Whenever I feel the urge to emotionally eat, I grab one of them and start reading. All the articles about weight loss success, health tips, fitness routines, etc. inspire me so much that I am motivated to NOT reach for food and stay on track with my health goals.*"

If you prefer having ONE go-to move, great! What do you want to do?
Examples: walk outside, do yoga for at least 20 minutes, start knitting, etc.

_____

_____

_____

_____

[1] Name changed for privacy.

Worksheet: PLEASE

Emotional eating negatively affects your physical health and vice versa.[47] As such, it is important that you take care of your body.

PL	**Treat Physical iLlness immediately.** Not feeling well? If you are sick or suffering from an illness, go and seek medical help immediately and take any prescribed medications. I would also advise reaching out to a friend, family member, or loved one so you are not alone during your illness. If you do not want professional medical help, consider a holistic approach to getting well, such as engaging in reiki, acupuncture, aromatherapy, acupressure, yoga, etc. The objective is to improve your health as soon as possible so it does not worsen. **Tip**: Do not skip seeing your doctor for a yearly checkup to avoid physical ailments.
E	**Eat a balanced diet.** What does a "balanced diet" look like? According to the Healthy Eating Plate: ½ of your plate should be made up of fruits and vegetables, ¼ should be whole grains, and the final ¼ should be protein.[48] One way to ensure that you are consuming healthy meals is to develop the habit of meal planning and prepping. If you do not know how, please see Quick Guide to Meal Planning and Prepping on page 112.

A	**A**void unhealthy substances. Unhealthy substances such as alcohol and prohibited drugs are considered "mood-altering" and can lower your resistance to negative emotions. For example, when you have had one too many glasses of wine, your resolve to not eat emotionally might be low. So, as you try to unlearn emotional eating, avoid unhealthy substances. If you are used to a glass of wine after a meal, switch to a healthier drink such as tea or coffee. Do the same when dining out.
S	**S**leep. Some research shows a link between sleep deprivation and emotional eating.[49] Others show a link between sleep deprivation and the propensity to reach for junk foods,[50] while others indicate that not getting enough sleep makes it harder for people to exercise self-control when it comes to food.[51] All this points to the need to get enough sleep! But how much is enough? According to the American Academy of Sleep Medicine and Sleep Research Society, adults need seven (7) or more hours of quality sleep nightly.[52] **Tip**: Not getting enough quality sleep? See How to Establish a Sleep Routine on page 151.

Exercise.

There are plenty of reasons to engage in physical activities. For instance, it gives one a feeling of mastery. This, in turn, improves self-esteem, which is one of the possible causes of emotional eating. Additionally, being fit makes it easier to remain fit and avoid mindless eating. Also, if you emotionally eat out of boredom or loneliness, exercising can eliminate these.

As a general rule of thumb, aim to exercise for at least 30 minutes daily. If you are a beginner or have not worked out in a while, start with shorter, less strenuous activities like walking or power walking for 10 minutes, and work your way up.

Keep in mind that consistency is key! So whatever physical activity you choose, make it a habit to keep on doing it!

Chapter 6: Interpersonal Effectiveness Skills for Emotional Eating

---

"Asking for help isn't giving up, it's refusing to give up."
— Unknown

Introduction to Interpersonal Effectiveness

Emotions make us human, but relationships make life meaningful. As such, learning Interpersonal Effectiveness skills are crucial to your healing journey. Although there are various reasons for emotional eating, for the most part, it is a learned behavior. To unlearn this behavior, you need the help and support of other people.

The people around us greatly affect our thoughts, feelings, and actions. Motivational speaker, author, and entrepreneur Jim Rohn said, *"You are the average of the five people you spend the most time with."* Some research shows that it goes one connection beyond that.[53] For example, if your mom's sister is an emotional eater, there is also a chance you will become an emotional eater. Dr. Mark Hyman, an American physician and author of books in the nutrition and longevity niche, also said, *"... the social threads that connect us might, in the end, be more important than genetics."*

So, the people around you influence your relationship with food whether you like it or not. And as you try to step away from emotional eating, it is critical that they understand, accept, and support you. Unfortunately, this is not always easy.

For example, a couple of years back, my mom visited me and basically cleared my kitchen cupboards of all my healthy food items and replaced them with unhealthier options while I was at work. She did this because she was unfamiliar with what I had in stock, which in her mind, meant I was not eating well. (By the way, in Chinese culture, it is common for parents to invade their children's privacy like this.) I had to reiterate my boundaries concerning my kitchen and the food I like to eat repeatedly.

If the British have afternoon tea, the Germans have a strong *Kaffee und kuchen* (coffee and cake) culture. So, my German friend Abigail[2] found it difficult to say "No" and explain to her parents that since she always has late lunches at work, she did not want coffee and cake whenever she made any afternoon visits. She told me her father got upset that she was not respecting a long-standing, beloved tradition. "*I tried cajoling, manipulating, even getting angry, but it didn't work. However, I am a social worker and was exposed to DBT at one point. When I got to the section about Interpersonal Effectiveness, I thought I would apply the techniques I learned, and it worked!*"

Importance of Healthy Relationships in Recovering from Emotional Eating

The importance of healthy relationships in recovery from emotional eating cannot be overstated. Here are a few specific ways that healthy relationships can support you:

1. **Emotional support and comfort**. When we have healthy relationships, we have people we can turn to for emotional support when triggered to emotionally eat. Friends, family, and loved ones can replace food as a source of comfort.

---

[2] Name changed for privacy.

2. **Accountability**. When we have healthy relationships, we have people who can hold us accountable to our goals and commitments. This can be particularly helpful in recovery from emotional eating, as it can help us stay on track to manage our emotions and develop healthier coping mechanisms.

   If you have people in your life that enable your emotional eating, consider removing them from your inner circle, at least for the time being. If this is not possible, as it is with immediate family members or colleagues, then try to minimize your time with them.

3. **Social connection**. You do not need to go on your healing journey alone. Healthy relationships provide opportunities for social connection, reducing feelings of loneliness and isolation. Supportive social connections also foster a sense of camaraderie. Knowing that others support you is a huge lift, even if they are not fighting the same struggle.

   Keep in mind that starting and establishing social connections start with you. That is, be proactive and seek opportunities to meet people rather than waiting for others to find you. How? Here are a few ideas: do volunteer work, attend online or offline classes or workshops, join online or offline emotional eating support groups, join clubs or groups that cater to your hobbies, etc.

4. **Self-esteem**. Healthy relationships can help improve our self-esteem and sense of self-worth. This can be particularly important for individuals who struggle with emotional eating, as low self-esteem and negative self-talk can be major contributors to emotional eating behaviors. For example, someone saying, "You got this!" is a great moral boost.

Struggling with self-esteem? Here are a few tips to boost your confidence:

- Practice self-care (e.g., take mental breaks throughout the day, get enough sleep, meditate, etc.)
- Set and undertake small, achievable goals (e.g., increase your number of steps per day, say "Hi" to people you don't know, drink more water, etc.)
- Practice self-compassion (e.g., avoid negative self-talk, practice gratitude, treat yourself like a friend, etc.)
- Reflect on your accomplishments, big or small.

The Interpersonal Effectiveness exercises on the following pages will help you develop effective communication and relationship skills that will help you have the right support on your journey.

Worksheet: Communicating Boundaries

Do you struggle to communicate your wants and needs for your emotional eating journey? If so, you are not alone. Many people do not tell others about wanting to recover from emotional eating for various reasons. This may include fear of rejection and disapproval, wanting to avoid conflict, or difficulty asserting boundaries. However, if you do not communicate your boundaries, they will keep getting crossed, making your healing journey more difficult.

Here's an example of a step-by-step boundary-setting exercise for emotional eaters:

1. Identify a specific situation in which you tend to engage in emotional eating.

   Example: A few hours after dinner, my partner and I tend to hibernate on the sofa after a long day's work. We might be watching something together or doing different things. Still, there is always an assortment of snacks (e.g., roasted nuts, chips, cheese, crackers, pretzels, etc.) on the coffee table for us to munch on.

   _____

   _____

   _____

   _____

   _____

   _____

2. Write down how you typically respond in this situation. This could include thoughts, feelings, and behaviors related to emotional eating.

_____

_____

_____

_____

_____

_____

3. Identify the boundary you would like to set in this situation.

Example: Since the birth of our second child (five years ago), I have been battling weight and body image issues. I realized that I have been turning more and more to food to cope, which, of course, worsens my situation. So want to limit the amount of junk food we keep in our house. Of course, I want to keep our together time at night, but I don't want to do the mindless late-night munching anymore.

_____

_____

_____

_____

_____

_____

4. Write down your boundary in a clear, specific, and assertive manner.

Examples:
I will only keep healthy snacks in the house and avoid buying junk food. But, before I do, I will communicate with my husband what I am feeling and why.

I will encourage my husband to do the same. But it's okay if he doesn't want to change because this is about me.

I will say "No" when my husband offers me late-night snacks.

_____

_____

_____

_____

_____

_____

5. Practice communicating your boundary assertively with someone you trust. This will help you feel more sure of yourself and ready to talk about your limits when the time comes.

6. Enact your boundary in the identified situation.

   Examples:
   If my husband offers me late-night snacks, I will always say these words, "No, but thanks, babe."
   If I find the snacks too tempting, I will do <u>*Take 5*</u> *(page 39) or any of the* <u>*Distress Tolerance*</u> *exercises (page 52) I've learned.*

7. Evaluate the effectiveness of your boundary and adjust as needed. If your boundary was effective, continue to practice it in similar situations. If it was ineffective, re-evaluate your boundary; perhaps there is another way or angle to enforce it. If you are still at a loss, seek the advice of someone you trust or a mental health professional.

Remember that setting boundaries is a process that may take time and practice to find what works best for you. Be patient and compassionate with yourself.

Worksheet: DEARMAN

DEARMAN is about *objective effectiveness*. It is the ability to successfully and clearly explain what you want to get out of a conversation. You see, there is an art to asking. If you demand, you will likely not obtain what you want, possibly harming your relationships. **DEARMAN** will assist you in asking effectively.

D	**D**escribe the situation What do you want or need to happen? Discuss the situation in simple, straightforward language. Say what you know to be true, not what you believe or feel. What's the situation? *Example: Mom/dad, please stop questioning my new food choices and eating behavior. I would also appreciate it if you didn't call the whole family and "update" them about what I'm doing.* _____ _____ _____ _____ _____
E	**E**xpress how you feel Begin your sentences with "I." Remember that you are discussing how you feel and what you think. People may interpret "You" remarks as accusations, increasing the likelihood of tension in the conversation. *Example: I want to change my eating habits and relationship with food to live happier and healthier.*

Assert yourself

Express your intentions without being confrontational. You do not want to get into an argument. You want to be heard clearly and efficiently.

Example: I know you care about me, but THIS is what is good for me right now.

A

_____

_____

_____

_____

_____

Reinforce your request

Make it obvious to the other person how important your request is to you. Also, thank them immediately if they give in to what you want.

R

Example: This is really important to me. I have been struggling for a long time and would appreciate your support.

_____
_____
_____
_____
_____

Mindfulness

Be mindful of what you want out of the conversation. Whatever the other person says, stay on track and keep your viewpoint. Others may object, insist, dismiss, or dispute with you if they disagree. Whatever they do, do not be persuaded, and stick to your guns!

M

Example: I hear you, mom/dad. I hope you hear too that the way I was eating before was not beneficial for me; I am now making changes that I know are good for me.

_____
_____
_____
_____

Appear confident

A

Do not show any sign of weakness in your argument. Demonstrate confidence through verbal and nonverbal signs, but do not be intimidating. Do not raise your voice or "stare down" the people you are talking to. Remember to be consistent as well. For example, do not slouch your shoulders after expressing your request or look nervous.

How do you want to show confidence?

Example: In a confident voice, say, "I hope you understand because I'm not going to change my mind on this."

_____

_____

_____

_____

_____

Negotiate

If the other person(s) still refuses to grant your request, it is time to negotiate. This will give you enough time to come up with a viable answer. You might suggest how to proceed or ask the other person what they think should happen next.

Examples:
How about we avoid the topic of my eating whenever I visit? What do you think?

_____

_____

_____

_____

_____

Worksheet: GIVE

GIVE is about relationship effectiveness. It is the ability to keep great relationships with others by fostering positive interactions. Simply put, you want the other person to feel good about your conversation so that they will be more likely to approve your request.

Be Gentle.

When asking someone to support you in your journey, you should do so with kindness. Demanding to be respected achieves disrespect. Also, do not say or do anything that could make the other person feel bad. Simply put—be nice!

List five ways to ask for something in a nice way.

Example: I'm trying to change my eating habits to better manage my emotions. Can you help me by not bringing unhealthy foods into the house?

1. _____
2. _____
3. _____
4. _____
5. _____

Act Interested.

If you want the other person to hear you, you must show that you hear them too. When the other person is talking, pay attention and ensure you understand their perspective.

List five ways you convey interest.

Examples: maintain eye contact during the conversation, don't interrupt, don't do other things, etc.

1. _____
2. _____
3. _____
4. _____
5. _____

Validate.

Show that you understand what the other person is thinking and feeling.

List five ways you validate others.

Examples: repeat what the other person said, look interested (not bored), etc.

1. _____
2. _____
3. _____
4. _____
5. _____

Show an Easy Manner.

Be friendly. Remember, you are making a request, not telling others what to do. People will feel more at ease and open to what you want if you maintain a friendly demeanor.

List 5 ways you can show friendliness.

Examples: smile, adopt a calm and friendly voice, etc.

1. _____
2. _____
3. _____
4. _____
5. _____

Worksheet: FAST

FAST is about maintaining your self-respect during difficult conversations. It is the ability to protect yourself from betraying your values and beliefs to receive approval or get what you want. **FAST** should be applied when you make a request and the other party is not agreeing (at least, not yet) or when someone insists on a request you do not want to grant because it goes against your values.

Be Fair.

When making a request, be fair to yourself and others. For example, as you make your request, ensure it is not something the other person cannot grant. Also, make sure to ask politely. Make no demands or make the other person feel frightened or guilty if they refuse to comply with your request.

F

Practice making a request fairly and reasonably.

Example: I've been struggling with emotional eating lately and could use some support. Would you be willing to listen when I feel stressed or upset?

_____

_____

_____

_____

_____

No Apologies.

Don't say sorry or apologize excessively. There is no need to feel apologetic when making a request, and there is no need to apologize if you want to say "No" to someone.

Practice making a request without apologizing:

Example: I've been struggling with emotional eating lately and could use some support. Would you be willing to listen when I feel stressed or upset?

NOT: I'm so sorry to ask this of you. I know you're busy. Geez, I feel really bad for asking.

_____

_____

_____

_____

_____

Practice saying "No" without apologizing:

Example: I don't want more food, thank you.

NOT: I am so sorry, I don't mean to offend you, but I am so full and cannot eat anymore. Sorry!

_____

_____

_____

_____

_____

A

Stick to your <u>V</u>alues.

Do not betray your values because the other person does not agree with your request. Also, do not sacrifice your convictions because someone pressures you to say "Yes" to something.

Practice sticking to your values when making a request.
Example: I understand you want to continue bringing junk food to our house. I just wanted to let you know that I plan to stop eating them from now on. And I would appreciate your love and support if you didn't eat them in front of me.

_____

_____

_____

_____

_____

Practice sticking to your values and saying "No" no matter what the other person says, does, or tries to get you to do.
Example: No, I will not make and bring fried chicken wings on your birthday. You know I'm a vegetarian.

_____

_____

_____

_____

_____

S

Be Truthful.

When making a request or denying one, be honest about your reasons. Do not lie, dramatize or exaggerate to get what you want or avoid doing what you do not want to do.

Practice honesty when making a request:

Example: I've been struggling with my relationship with food and want to stop my emotional eating. This is why I don't want junk food in the house.

_____

_____

_____

_____

_____

Practice honesty when saying "No:

Example: [when offered food you don't want to eat] No, thank you.

NOT: [when offered food you don't want to eat] Oh! I really, really want to, but I just had the biggest meal!

_____

_____

_____

_____

_____

Chapter 7: Developing Healthy Habits

"If you always do what you've always done,
you always get what you've always gotten."— Jessie Potter

Healthy living helps prevent emotional eating because it promotes physical and emotional wellbeing. As mentioned, emotional eating is usually a coping mechanism for unpleasant or negative emotions. However, life has ups and downs, so you cannot eliminate unpleasant situations and emotions. What you can do, in addition to the DBT skills you have learned, is strengthen your emotional resilience so that you can cope and manage life's obstacles while maintaining a sense of well-being. This chapter explores various effective ways to develop healthy habits. These practices will not only help you overcome emotional eating. They also have the power to impact every aspect of your life positively.

Top 10 Healthy Food and Eating Habits

Emotional eating and unhealthy eating habits reinforce each other. Adopting healthy food and eating habits helps prevent this maladaptive behavior by helping to stabilize your blood sugar levels, improve your mood, reduce cravings, prevent you from undertaking restrictive diets, etc. Following are 10 tips regarding food and meals that can help your journey:

1. **Make <u>mindful eating</u> (page 41) a way of life**. Eating mindfully helps you become more aware of your eating habits and the sensations of hunger and fullness in your body. By paying attention to *what* and *how* you eat, you can develop a healthier relationship with food and reduce the likelihood of

emotional eating and overeating. This practice can also help you enjoy your food more fully and appreciate the sensory experience of eating.

2. **Practice portion control**. Switch to smaller plates, bowls, and cups to help control your portions and avoid overeating. You can also try using divided plates to separate your food into different groups. This way, you can get a balanced meal with all the nutrients your body needs. If you are a "snacker," use divided snack plates. This way, even if you do emotionally eat, you can "trick" your brain by only filling one part with something unhealthy (e.g., chips, mini pretzels, etc.) while filling the rest with healthy snacks such as cut-up vegetables, unsalted and unroasted nuts, etc.

3. **Keep healthy snacks on hand**. Keep healthy snacks like fruits, vegetables, and nuts on hand to help curb cravings. **Tip**: Make reaching for healthy snacks an easy choice by (1) getting rid of unhealthy ones (e.g., cookies, chips, soda, etc.) in your home and (2) pre-cutting fruits and veggies into bite-size portions you can store in your fridge.

   Are you a "junk food snacker?" If your emotions make you crave something sweet, salty, or savory, look for healthier alternatives. For example, switch from potato chips to air-popped popcorn, processed chicken nuggets to homemade ones, ice cream to frozen yogurt with berries, etc.

4. **Drink a lot of water**. Drinking enough water can help you feel full and hydrated, which can help prevent reaching for food. Additionally, research shows that water improves mood![54,55]

   The amount of water that should be consumed depends on various parameters, including age, gender, weight, activity level, and climate. The National Academies of Sciences, Engineering, and Medicine suggests that men strive to drink around 3.7 liters (125 ounces) daily, while women aim for a total daily water intake of around 2.7 liters (91 ounces).[56] It is important to note that this recommendation includes all water sources, including water from beverages and food. So, if you consume plenty of water-rich foods and beverages throughout the day, you may not need to drink as much plain water to meet your daily needs.

Hate drinking plain water? Try *infused water*. For example, add ginger and mint, watermelon slices, or various citrus fruits and peels to your water.

5. **Avoid skipping meals**. Skipping meals can make you hangry (hungry+angry) and lead to emotional eating AND overeating later in the day. So, make sure to eat regular meals and snacks to help regulate physical hunger. To do this, space out your meals so you can eat every 3-4 hours. For example, have breakfast at 8 AM, a mid-morning snack at 10:30 AM, lunch at 1:00 PM, an after snack at 3:30 PM, dinner at 6:30 PM, and an evening snack at 8:30 PM.

6. **Eat protein-rich foods**. Protein-rich foods like lean meats, eggs, and legumes can help you feel full and satisfied. Further, research suggests that consuming protein-rich foods can help improve mood and reduce symptoms of depression and anxiety.[57,58]

The suggested daily protein consumption varies depending on age, gender, weight, exercise level, and overall health. However, as a general rule of thumb, the recommended daily protein intake is 56 grams per day for men and 46 grams per day for women.[59] If you are vegan, you can still meet this requirement by consuming protein-rich foods such as pulses, soy products (e.g., tofu, tempeh, etc.), nuts and seeds (e.g., almonds, walnuts, chia seeds, etc.), whole grains (e.g., brown rice, oats, etc.), plant-based protein powders, etc.

7. **Do NOT grocery shop when hungry.** Shopping for groceries while hungry can lead to impulsive purchases of unhealthy snacks or comfort foods that you may regret later. You can make more rational and healthy food choices by avoiding grocery shopping when hungry. Furthermore, shopping while hungry can lead to overbuying, contributing to food waste and raising overall food costs.

8. **Develop a daily eating routine.** A regular eating schedule helps prevent skipping meals, overeating, and the likelihood of impulsive or emotional eating. A routine also helps stabilize your blood sugar levels and reduce cravings for sugary or high-fat foods. Lastly, it can help you establish structure and predictability in your daily life, reducing stress, anxiety, and other unpleasant emotions. (See also Quick Guide to Meal Planning and Prepping below.)

9. **Practice self-compassion (page 66).** Be kind and compassionate to yourself if you slip up and emotionally eat. Avoid negative self-talk and focus on making healthier choices moving forward.

10. **Keep a food journal.** Starting and maintaining a food journal can help you identify patterns in your eating habits and help you make healthier choices. (See also Identifying Your Emotional Triggers, page 75.)

When changing your food and eating habits, refrain from thinking about what you are "giving up" and focus instead on what you are gaining—a healthier mind and body!

Quick Guide to Meal Planning and Prepping

Meal planning and prepping can be particularly helpful for individuals struggling with emotional eating. Otherwise, there is a risk that you will revert to old eating habits because that is what you know; that is what is easy and comfortable to do. Here are other reasons why meal planning and prepping are advantageous:

1. **Reduces decision fatigue**. Deciding what to eat can feel overwhelming when you are mentally or emotionally exhausted. By having a pre-planned menu, you can avoid decision fatigue and the temptation to turn to unhealthy foods when you feel overwhelmed.

2. **Provides structure and routine**. For many, emotional eating can be triggered by a lack of structure or routine in their daily lives. Meal planning and prepping can provide a sense of structure and routine around meal times, which can help to reduce the likelihood of emotional eating.

3. **Encourages healthy food choices**. Meal planning and prepping can help you make healthier food choices by providing a framework for meal times. By planning and preparing your meals in advance, you can ensure that you incorporate various healthy foods into your diet.

4. **Reduces stress around meal times**. By having pre-prepared meals or components of meals, you can reduce the stress associated with meal times. You do not have to worry about what to cook, missing ingredients, etc., and you can quickly assemble a meal when hungry.

5. **Increases feelings of control**. Emotional eating often feels like you do not have control. Meal planning and prepping can provide that sense of control over food choices, which can be empowering for individuals struggling with emotional eating.

Note: Meal planning and prepping is a broad topic beyond this book's scope. Still, I have added the sections below as a guide to jumpstart this healthy habit for you.

What is Meal Planning?

Meal planning is deciding in advance what meals you will eat for a set period, typically a week or two, and then creating a shopping list based on those meals. Meal planning aims to ensure that you have healthy, nutritious meals available throughout the week while reducing the time, effort, and stress associated with meal preparation.

Meal planning typically involves several steps:

1. **Decide on the meals you want** to prepare for the week, considering your dietary needs and preferences. Do not rush this process. Choose a time when you are calm and comfortable and have enough time to plan at least a week's worth of meals. (**Tip:** Don't meal plan when you are hungry!) Make the plan or menu as detailed as you can. Include what you want to eat for breakfast, lunch, dinner, and snacks and when you should be eating these meals.

2. **Create a grocery list** of the ingredients you will need for your meals. **Tip**: This will most likely require you to review your kitchen cupboards to see what you have. Use the opportunity to get rid of unhealthy and expired food items.

3. **Shop for the groceries on your list**. Do this when you are not hungry so you are not tempted to reach for anything beyond what is on your list.

4. At home, **place your groceries where you can easily see and reach them**. Remember, make healthy food an easy choice for you! For example,

put fruits on your table, vegetables at the front of your fridge, nuts and seeds in clear glass jars, and put them at the front of your cupboards, etc.

5. **Stick to your meal plan** throughout the week, adjusting only when necessary for changes in your schedule or unexpected events.

What is Meal Prepping?

Meal prepping is preparing meals or portions of meals in advance, typically for a week's worth of meals at a time. The meals are usually pre-cooked, portioned, and stored in the fridge or freezer until ready to be consumed. Meal prepping can involve cooking entire meals, such as casseroles or stir-fries, or preparing components of meals, such as grilled chicken, roasted vegetables, or cooked grains that can be assembled into a full meal on a later date.

Meal prepping is often done in one batch on a designated day each week, and it can save time, money, and stress around meal times. By having pre-cooked meals or components readily available, you can avoid making impulsive and potentially unhealthy food choices when pressed for time or feeling stressed.

Here are some common components of meal prepping:

1. **Cooking proteins**. This can include grilling chicken breasts, cooking ground turkey or beef, roasting fish, or preparing tofu or tempeh.

2. **Preparing grains**. This can include cooking rice, quinoa, or other grains in advance for various meals throughout the week.

3. **Prepping vegetables**. This can include washing, chopping, and roasting or steaming vegetables to be used in salads, stir-fries, or as side dishes.

4. **Preparing snacks**. This can include cutting up fruits and vegetables, portioning out nuts and seeds, or making energy bites or protein bars to have on hand for quick snacks.

5. **Assembling meals**. This can include putting together salads, stir-fries, or other meals in advance and storing them in containers to be grabbed and eaten or reheated and consumed throughout the week.

If this is the first time you are food planning and prepping, start with easy meals you know how to prepare so you do not get overwhelmed. Also, you do not always have to come up with different meals.

For example, some people are perfectly okay with having the same breakfast for a week. I usually eat the same breakfast each day: oatmeal or granola with whole-wheat toast and a piece of fruit. The routine is easy and calming and ensures I get a healthy breakfast.

Incorporate Physical Activity into Your Routine

Physical activities can help prevent emotional eating by reducing stress, improving mood, and boosting self-esteem.[60,61] Regular exercise can also improve sleep quality[62], which is important for managing appetite, reducing cravings for unhealthy foods, and regulating emotions. Additionally, exercise can *replace* food as a coping mechanism when mentally and emotionally overwhelmed.

Here are 10 tips for incorporating physical activity into your routine:

1. **Make engaging in physical activities an EASY choice.** If you think working out is hard, you might not do it even if you want to. So remove any barriers that might make it hard to choose to exercise. For example, choose a gym or fitness center near your home or workplace. If you prefer to work at

home, invest in some basic equipment, such as resistance bands or dumbbells, so you do not feel limited. If you prefer to exercise first thing in the morning, lay out your workout clothing the night before by your bed. In short, make exercising convenient for yourself.

2. **Start small**. If you are new to exercising, start with small, manageable goals. This could be as simple as taking a 10-minute walk each day and gradually increasing the duration and intensity of your workouts over time.

3. **Set realistic goals**. No one begins mountain climbing by taking on Mount Everest. So, set goals that are achievable for you. For example, walking for 30 minutes three times per week.

4. **Find an activity you enjoy**. This could be anything from walking or jogging to swimming or dancing. When you enjoy the activity, you are more likely to stick with it.

5. **Schedule it in**. Treat exercise as an important appointment and schedule it into your daily routine. This could be first thing in the morning, during your lunch break, or after work.

6. **Create opportunities to move.** One of the primary reasons people cite for not exercising is "lack of time." Many people lead busy lives with work, family, and other commitments, so it can be difficult to find time for exercise. Even so, find "pockets of opportunity" within your day. For example, take breaks throughout the day to stretch or take a short walk, use the stairs instead of the elevator, and park your car further than usual to ensure you walk.

7. **Mix it up**. Incorporate various exercises into your routine to prevent boredom and keep things interesting. For example, start with a 5-min

warmup, followed by 20 minutes of cardio, 15 minutes of strength training, and end with a 5-min cooldown.

8. **Make it a family affair or a social activity**. If possible, involve your family in physical activities like walking in nature or riding a bike together. Join a fitness class or find a workout buddy to help keep you motivated.

9. **Use technology**. Use fitness apps like Olson Applications' _5 Minute Home Workouts_, Workout Apps' _7 Minute Workout_, FitOn's _FitOn Workouts_, and others to easily squeeze in quick workouts whenever you have a few spare minutes. Invest in wearable devices, such as inexpensive step counters to FitBit watches, to set exercise goals and track progress.

10. **Focus on the benefits!** Remind yourself of the advantages of exercise, such as increased mood and energy, decreased stress, improved sleep, and less susceptibility to emotional eating. Concentrating on the good consequences will help you to get started.

Manage Daily Stress through Healthy Coping Mechanisms

Stress is one of the leading triggers for emotional eating. As such, stress management techniques can be extremely helpful in reducing this behavior. Here are 12 tips for managing daily stress:

1. **Practice mindfulness (page 37)**. Mindful breathing, meditation, mindful eating, hitting "Pause" during the day, sitting still for a few minutes, and other mindfulness practices help reduce stress and improve focus. Make it easy to start this practice by setting reminders throughout the day. You can use your phone and set the alarm every 60 minutes, reminding you to take a quick 5-10

minute break, or you can download and use apps such as Stand Up!. Desktop apps such as BreakTimer and Stretchly can help remind you to take a break when you are always in front of a computer.

2. **Exercise regularly**. Regular physical activity helps reduce cortisol, the stress hormone, in the body. At the same time, it releases endorphins, the feel-good hormone.

3. **Actively relax your muscles**. Stress causes muscle strain, causing tension headaches, backaches, and fatigue. Fight these physical manifestations of stress by stretching, getting a massage or massaging yourself, taking warm baths, etc. (**Tip**: See TIPP on page 62, and do Paced Breathing with Muscle Relaxation.)

4. **Get enough sleep**. Adequate sleep is essential for managing stress and promoting overall health. (See also How to Establish a Sleep Routine, page 151.)

5. **Stay organized**. Keeping a schedule and staying organized can help reduce stress and improve productivity. Use a planner or organization system to create a daily routine to establish structure and reduce decision fatigue. You can use a simple notepad or journal or apps like Microsoft To Do or Trello.

6. **Take multiple mental breaks during the day**. Step away from your normal activities and allow yourself to relax and recharge. Examples: go for a short walk, do Take 5 (page 39), listen to music, do a 5-minute yoga routine, etc.

7. **Take breaks from social media and news consumption**. Constant exposure to negative news stories and social media can be overwhelming,

contributing to feelings of stress and anxiety. Take breaks that promote relaxation, such as walking in nature, cuddling your pet, watering your plants, etc.

8. **Say "No."** Protect yourself, your time, and your sanity by learning the power of saying "No." It takes time and effort to heal from emotional eating, so focus on yourself now. If this is hard for you, start by saying "No" to small requests or invitations, and work up to bigger ones. For example, say, "*I can't join you for coffee, but thanks!*" before moving on to something like, "*I can't add any more to my workload.*" (See also Communicating Boundaries, page 95.)

Here are some other tips to help you say "No."

- **Use "I" statements** to explain why you say "No." For example, "*I'm unable to commit to that right now because I have other priorities.*"
- **Be clear and direct** when saying "No." It is important to be clear and direct in your response. Avoid being vague or giving mixed signals. For example, "*I can't accept that new task. I have enough on my plate right now.*"
- **Say "No" without being rude or aggressive**. Be firm but polite in your response, and avoid apologizing excessively or over-explaining yourself. For example, say, "*I can't join you guys for dinner this weekend because I already have plans,*" instead of, "*I'm so sorry! I already have plans this weekend. Oh my, I feel bad. Please don't be mad, guys.*"
- **Offer alternatives.** If you are declining an invitation or request, offer an alternative solution. For example, "*I can't make it to the party, but maybe we can grab coffee next week instead.*"

9. **Give yourself joy**. Engage in hobbies or activities that bring you happiness. Many people forego simple pleasures for various reasons: lack of time, fear of

being judged, prioritizing others or other responsibilities, family or societal pressure, etc. However, life is too short not to enjoy it! So, even when your schedule is tight, find ways to do something for yourself (e.g., read a few pages of a book, shower and sing your heart out, dance while cooking, etc.)

10. **Connect with others.** Spend time with family and friends to promote feelings of connection and support. For example, call a friend or family member you have not talked to in a while or message people to say "Hi" and find out how they are doing.

11. **Practice gratitude**. Focus on the things you are grateful to shift your focus away from stress. (See also Reflection and Gratitude Practice, page 138.)

12. **Seek support if needed**. If stress becomes overwhelming, consider seeking support from a mental health professional or support group.

Chapter 8: Building a Support System

"Surround yourself with only people who are going to lift you higher."— Oprah Winfrey

Emotional eating involves using food as a coping mechanism for emotions; breaking that pattern can be very difficult without the help and support of others. Many people like to "carry the load" on their own. However, is it also not true that most people are more than willing to extend a helping hand when asked? So, remember that you do not need to suffer the weight of your healing journey alone. Reach out to others because they have the power to make your recovery easier.

Cultivate a Supportive Inner Voice (Self)

Before you seek support from others, ensure that you support your efforts. Developing a supportive inner voice is practicing self-compassion and learning to speak to yourself in a kind, encouraging, and supportive manner. It also entails treating any self-sabotaging behaviors.

Self-Sabotage – What You May Be THINKING

Several beliefs may be sabotaging your success with emotional eating, including:

All-or-nothing mentality. This is the belief that everything you do must be "perfect" to change your eating habits. This can lead to feelings of failure and frustration, leading to emotional eating.

> **What to do:** Shift your mindset from black or white to shades of gray. Accept that healing is not a linear process and that there will be good and

bad moments. Do not worry about being perfect. Just do your best one step at a time.

Negative self-talk. Negative self-talk involves the critical and negative messages you tell yourself. This can include thoughts like "*I'll never be able to control my eating habits*," "*I'm not good enough to make positive changes in my life,*" or "*I doubt I can do this.*"

>   **What to do:** Practice <u>Self-Compassion, Self-Forgiveness, and Self-Validation</u>, page 66.

Believing that food is the ONLY WAY to cope with emotions. The word "comfort foods" exist for a reason, but food is NOT the only thing that can bring comfort and help you deal with your emotions.

>   **What to do:** See the chapter on <u>Emotion Regulation</u>, page 65.

"I don't deserve..." mentality. There is a great deal of shame and guilt associated with emotional eating. As a result, you may develop the mindset that you do not deserve to be happy or do not deserve to take care of yourself or make good choices because you believe you are unworthy, flawed, or incompetent.

>   **What to do:** Practice self-care, <u>self-compassion</u> (page 66), and building your <u>self-esteem</u> (page 93).

Self-Sabotage – What You May Be DOING

Apart from any self-sabotaging thoughts, you may also be countering your efforts by doing any of the following:

"Holding on" to unhealthy food items. As much as possible, remove all temptations in your home. Think: if you cannot see it, you cannot eat it. If you find it a waste to throw these food items, donate them.

Buying "emergency comfort foods." When grocery shopping, refrain from buying the things that you usually consume when you emotionally eat. Some people like to keep an "emergency stash," but you see, that means you are expecting yourself to fail. Instead, expect yourself to succeed! And if something truly unpleasant happens: practice Mindfulness (page 37) + Distress Tolerance (page 52) + Emotion Regulation (page 65).

Staying around "enablers." Not everyone will be supportive of your journey. Some may not understand you; some may secretly envy you, while others may have unhealthy eating habits and feel uncomfortable or threatened by your healthier choices. Of course, it is unfortunate if the people you love do not support you. Still, it can be damaging if they undermine your efforts. Examples: a family member constantly offering unhealthy food or drinks, friends who encourage you to emotionally eat with them, co-workers who "joke" about you no longer being sociable because of your new eating habits, etc. The best way to handle these people is to steer clear of them. If this is not possible, limit the time you spend with them.

Build Your Support Circle (Others)

Support from others can provide a sense of accountability, encouragement, and motivation. Support from family, friends, or a support group can help you feel less alone in your struggle and provide a safe space to share experiences and emotions. It can also provide practical assistance, such as help with meal planning and preparation or finding alternative coping mechanisms.

Creating a support circle involves identifying people who can offer assistance. Here are some steps to help you create your support circle:

1. **Identify the support you need.** Consider what kind of support you need and what types of people can provide that support. Reflect on the list below to help you figure out what you need.

   - ☐ **Moral support.** Do you need people who regularly check in to see how you are doing?
   - ☐ **Physical support.** Do you need others' physical presence in your journey, such as a fitness buddy or another person trying to heal from emotional eating or an eating disorder?
   - ☐ **Emotional support.** Do you need someone to listen to you, understand your journey, and talk you through your emotions?
   - ☐ **Intellectual support.** Do you need someone who knows more than you know? Someone to give you tips and recommendations, or perhaps someone who has studied nutrition or eating behaviors.
   - ☐ **Resource support.** Do you need someone who can provide tangible and practical support? Examples: driving you to and from fitness or workout classes, babysitting your kids so you have time for yourself, helping you grocery shop for healthy food, sharing access to exercise equipment, etc.

2. **Reach out to friends and family.** After you identify what kind(s) of support you need, consider reaching out to friends and family members you feel comfortable talking to and who have shown themselves to be supportive. Explain what you are going through and ask if they would be willing to offer their support.

3. **Join a support group.** Look for local support groups or online communities focusing on your specific struggles or interests. These can provide a great source of comfort and understanding as you connect with others with similar experiences. For example, visit the websites of national eating disorder organizations like the National Eating Disorders Association (NEDA) or Eating Disorder Hope and use their search tools to find emotional eating support groups in your area. You can also use apps like MeetUp to look for online support groups in your country.

4. **Be open to new relationships.** Be open to meeting new people and building relationships with those who share your interests or struggles. You never know who may become an important part of your support circle.

5. **Consider a therapist.** A licensed therapist or counselor can provide a safe and supportive environment to work through your challenges and help you build the skills you need to heal. They can also help you identify additional resources or support that may be helpful.

As you go through the above steps, you may realize that certain people are not helpful (e.g., enables and saboteurs). In this case, you need to evaluate their presence in your life. If they are damaging to your journey, then perhaps it is time to let them go, at least for now.

Letting go of unsupportive people can be a difficult but necessary step to take. If you are struggling with this, here are some tips.

Firstly, **recognize and radically accept their impact** on your journey. Take a moment to reflect on how this unsupportive person affects your mental health, goals, and well-being. And even though it may be painful, acknowledge that their behavior is not conducive to your growth.

Secondly, try and **communicate your needs** if this is someone with whom you cannot or do not want to sever all ties (e.g., a close family member, childhood friend, etc.). Do not ghost these people and "disappear" from their lives. Let them know what you are going through, that their behavior is not helpful, and that you need their support. If communicating with an unsupportive person does not work, **set strong boundaries**. This may mean limiting your contact with them or avoiding certain topics when you are with them.

Lastly, if communicating your needs and setting boundaries do not work, it is time to **let them go with love**. Remember that you deserve to be surrounded by people who uplift and encourage you.
So, tell unsupportive people that you are prioritizing yourself right now, wish them well, and express your hope to possibly reconnect with them in the future.

Building a support system takes time and effort. It is important to be patient and persistent because you can make your healing journey easier with the right attitude and people by your side.

Chapter 9: Dealing with Setbacks and Relapses

"A setback is a setup for a comeback."— *T.D. Jakes*

Emotional eating can be difficult to break, and setbacks and relapses are common occurrences as you develop a healthier relationship with food. However, instead of feeling "defeated," it is important to recognize that setbacks and relapses are NOT signs of failure but a natural part of the healing process.

How to Prevent Setbacks

Social situations, such as parties, holidays, and family gatherings, can be challenging for those struggling with emotional eating. The abundance of food, pressure to indulge, and emotional triggers can make it difficult to keep up with your healthy eating habits. However, with the right strategies, navigating these situations and avoiding setbacks is possible.

One approach is to **plan ahead**. Before attending a social event, consider the types of foods that will be available and make a plan for what you will eat. Focus on healthy options, such as fruits and vegetables, lean protein, and whole grains. Bring a healthy dish to share, if possible, so you know at least one option will align with your goals.

If you are concerned more about the presence of certain people rather than the presence of certain food, again, plan ahead. Visualize encountering this person and what you are dreading from the conversation. Next, rehearse in your mind what you will say or do.

Who triggers you?

Example:

I always get triggered when my younger siblings ask why I still don't have "someone" in my life.

_____

_____

_____

_____

_____

What is your plan for dealing with this person?

Example: *(1) Do __STOP__ (page 59). (2) If my sisters persist in nagging me, I'll say, "I feel ridiculed when you guys always comment about me not having a partner. Why do you do that?" or "When you guys joke about me, it takes the fun out of these gatherings for me. I want to enjoy coming here, so please stop doing that."*

_____

_____

_____

_____

_____

Important: When you visualize the conversation, practice your plan over and over in your head or role-play with someone you trust. This will give you the courage to do it when the time comes.

Another approach is to **practice mindfulness** before, during, and after social events. Take the time to savor and enjoy your food rather than mindlessly consuming it. Listen to your body's natural hunger and fullness cues, and take breaks between bites to allow your body to register when satisfied. Mindful eating s not just something to do at home. It is something you can apply all the time whenever you are eating.

Focus on socializing, not avoiding food. Instead of making the event all about food, focus on socializing and spending time with friends and family. Engage in conversation and activities that do not involve food.

Another strategy is to **enlist the support of others**. Tell your friends and family about your goals and ask for their support in sticking to them. If someone offers you food you do not want to eat, politely decline or ask for a smaller portion.

Remember, it is okay to indulge in moderation. If there is a particular food that you love and want to enjoy, allow yourself a small serving. The key is to avoid overindulging and to stay mindful of your choices.

How to Recover from a Setback

Setbacks can happen anytime during your emotional eating journey despite your efforts to avoid them. When they do, keep the following in mind:

1. **Practice radical acceptance (page 27).** If a setback or relapse occurs, accept it. Remember, this already happened; no power on earth can undo it. To think about it over and over only prolongs your suffering.

2. **Reframe your thinking: setbacks are a necessary part of progress.** Do not think of setbacks as a step backward. Think of them as just a momentary pause in your progress. For example, suppose you have not emotionally eaten for months. However, something unexpected and tragic happened, and you spent the previous night emotionally eating. You did not forget all you learned or wasted the efforts of the previous months, right? So, you did not step backward and undo all your hard work. What counts now is what you do next.

3. **Practice self-compassion and self-forgiveness.** Be kind and gentle with yourself when you experience a setback or relapse. Avoid self-blame and negative self-talk. Recognize that it is natural to have challenges and difficulties in recovery.

4. **Do you need a break?** Do not rush to bounce back. You may feel exhausted, disappointed, and unmotivated when a setback occurs. It is okay to take a little break. Note, though, that taking a break does not mean engaging in emotional eating. Give yourself some TLC (tender loving care) and tell yourself that the setback is something you need to experience. Additionally, do not take a break for too long, as this may worsen feelings of guilt or shame over the setback, or you might slip back into unhealthy eating habits.

5. **Reconnect with your motivation.** Reflect on why you started your journey toward emotional eating recovery in the first place. Reconnect with your motivation by reminding yourself of the negative consequences of continued emotional eating. For example, consider how emotional eating has contributed to your weight gain and how this has negatively affected your ability to join family and friends in various physical activities (e.g., outdoor sports, gardening, etc.).

6. **Reflect on the trigger.** Identify the trigger that caused the setback or relapse. Was it a specific event, emotion, or thought? Understanding the trigger can help you create a plan to prevent future relapses.

   Example: Breaking up with my partner triggered my emotional eating.

7. **Reflect on what may have contributed to the setback apart from the trigger.** A relapse can be caused by a single trigger, but were there additional reasons for your emotional eating? For example, were you ill or under great stress, or do you not have a strong social network? If there are other contributing factors, see how you can address these as well.

   Example: The breakup happened while I had been stressed out about a major assignment at work for months. In the future, I must manage my stress better. I've always enjoyed yoga, but I've fallen out of practice over the years, and I believe I need to pick that up again.

8. **Create a plan**. Develop a plan for how you will get back on track. This might include revisiting the principles of mindful eating, scheduling more self-care time, or seeking professional support.

Example: (1) I'll visit my family over the weekend. I need to be surrounded by people who are supportive "constants" in my life. (2) I'll revisit my meal planning and prepping efforts because these practices helped me last time.

9. **Learn from the setback.** Use the setback as an opportunity to learn and grow. Reflect on what worked and what did not work. Use this knowledge to make adjustments to your plan so that you can better cope with future challenges.

   Example: I realize now that I became dependent on my partner, and our relationship became my only priority. If and when I get into another relationship, I'll make sure I have other people I give time and attention to in my life.

Setbacks and relapses are normal in the journey toward overcoming emotional eating. It is important to plan ahead to avoid them, but if they do occur, do not feel guilty or ashamed. Pick yourself up and carry on with your goals.

Chapter 10: Maintaining Long-Term Success

"Motivation is what gets you started. Habit is what keeps you going."— Jim Ryun

---

Maintaining a healthy relationship with food requires ongoing effort and commitment. Here we will cover key strategies and practices for sustaining your progress toward a healthier relationship with food.

Top 10 Strategies for Maintaining Healthy Eating Habits

1. **Continuously assess and manage your emotions**. As mentioned, emotions, pleasant and unpleasant, are what make us who we are. So, the goal is never to eliminate our feelings; the objective is how to better manage them. As such, it is important to always be "tuned in" with your emotions and identify any triggers that may lead to emotional eating. Also, whenever you desire to reach for food for comfort, turn to other coping mechanisms, such as journaling, practicing mindfulness, or engaging in stress-relieving activities.

2. **Embrace DBT concepts (Acceptance + Change) and skills (Mindfulness, Distress Tolerance, Emotion Regulation, and Interpersonal Effectiveness).** What you have learned here is not intended for one-time reading. Applying what you have read and practicing them when you do not need them is the key to applying them when necessary.

3. **Establish a healthy routine**. Establish a daily routine that includes healthy habits such as exercise, nutritious meals, and sufficient sleep. A routine can help you stay on track and make healthy choices easier and more automatic.

4. **Continue practicing mindful eating**. Make mindful eating a way of life. Eat with awareness, savor each drink and bite, and recognize hunger and fullness cues—all the time.

5. **Continue prioritizing yourself**. Accept that YOU are valuable and deserve a life free of the mental, emotional, physical, and financial costs associated with emotional eating. As you uplift yourself, it is possible that not everyone will support you, which is okay. Remember, this journey is yours, not theirs. So, establish boundaries, communicate what you need, and be okay with letting unsupportive people go, at least for now.

6. **Set realistic and achievable goals.** Breaking free from emotional eating or any other unhealthy behavior always seems like a mammoth task, leading you to feel overwhelmed. So, break long-term goals into smaller, manageable steps. And enjoy those small steps because each is part of your journey.

7. **Learn from setbacks**. Accept that setbacks and relapses are a normal part of the change process. Instead of feeling shame and regret, or getting mad, use setbacks as an opportunity to learn and grow.

8. **Stay connected with your support system**. Maintain contact with your support system, whether that is family, friends, or a therapist. Regular check-ins can help you stay accountable and motivated.

9. **Stay adaptable**. Be open to adjusting your goals and strategies as needed. Life is unpredictable, and circumstances may change, so it is important to be flexible and adaptable to maintain healthy habits.

10. **Set new goals!** Once you have achieved your initial goals, set new ones to continue growing and evolving in your recovery. For example, suppose your initial goal is to practice mindful eating. Once you are comfortable with it, aim to apply it daily. Now that you have a better appreciation for what you eat, perhaps the next goal is to try meal planning and prepping.

Celebrate Progress and Achievements with Non-Food Related Rewards

It is important to celebrate your progress for various reasons. Firstly, it **reinforces positive behaviors and habits** because it helps to solidify the connection between your efforts and the positive outcomes you have achieved, making it more likely that you will continue engaging in those behaviors. It also **contributes to your self-awareness**. Celebrating your progress is an opportunity to reflect on your journey and better understand your strengths and capabilities.

Celebrating your achievements, big and small, also **helps you maintain your commitment** to freedom from emotional eating. By acknowledging and honoring your progress, you create a positive association with the process of personal growth and transformation, making it more likely that you will continue working towards your goals.

But how do you celebrate? Many grow up associating progress, success, and milestones with food. However, while these associations are deeply ingrained, it is time for you to challenge them to develop healthier habits. Look at the list below, start reshaping your perception of success, and find other meaningful ways to celebrate your achievements.

Following are 35 non-food-related rewards. Check which ones appeal to you or are the easiest for you to do. Please feel free to add other ideas as well in the space provided.

- ☐ Take a bubble bath.
- ☐ Get a massage.
- ☐ Buy a new book.
- ☐ Watch a movie.
- ☐ Take a nap.
- ☐ Listen to music.
- ☐ Buy a new piece of clothing.
- ☐ Go for a walk.
- ☐ Treat yourself to a manicure or pedicure.
- ☐ Go on a weekend getaway.
- ☐ Visit a museum or art gallery.
- ☐ Buy a new plant for your home or office.
- ☐ Attend a concert or live performance.
- ☐ Take a yoga class.
- ☐ Buy yourself a new piece of jewelry.
- ☐ Spend time with a friend.
- ☐ Get a new haircut or style.
- ☐ Take a day trip to a nearby city or attraction.
- ☐ Start planning a vacation.
- ☐ Buy a new piece of art or home décor.
- ☐ Take a cooking class.
- ☐ Sign up for a dance class.
- ☐ Treat yourself to a spa day.
- ☐ Take a photography class.
- ☐ Buy a new journal or planner.
- ☐ Attend a sports game or event.
- ☐ Start meal planning and prepping.
- ☐ Let go of unsupportive people.
- ☐ Go on a hike.
- ☐ Visit a friend living in a different city.

- ☐ Spend a day exploring a new town or city.
- ☐ Try a new hobby or craft.
- ☐ Sign up for a fitness class or program.
- ☐ Buy yourself a new piece of technology or gadget.
- ☐ Spend a day volunteering for a cause you care about.
- ☐ Others:

_____

_____

_____

_____

_____

_____

Reflection and Gratitude Practice

As mentioned, emotional eating is about coping with difficult emotions or situations. By practicing reflection and gratitude, you can learn to identify and acknowledge your feelings more healthily, helping you avoid turning to food for comfort.

Reflection can help you become more aware of your emotional triggers and patterns, helping you develop strategies to manage them. By reflecting on past experiences and emotions, you can gain insight into *why* you turn to food for comfort or distraction and work on developing healthier coping mechanisms.

Gratitude can also be a powerful tool for managing emotional eating. When you focus on the good things in your life and cultivate a sense of gratitude, you are more likely to feel positive and hopeful, reducing your stress levels and making you less likely to turn to food to ease your stress.

Worksheet: Reflection and Gratitude

Here is a simple reflection and gratitude exercise that you can try:

1. Find a quiet and comfortable space where you will not be interrupted. Sit down and take a few deep breaths to center yourself.

2. Reflect on your day or week. Think about the things you accomplished, the challenges you faced, and the people you interacted with. Try to focus on the positive aspects of your experiences.

   Where are your thoughts taking you?

   Example: *I'm proud of myself for changing my eating patterns and how I feel about food.*

   _____

   _____

   _____

   _____

3. Take out a notebook or journal and write down three things you are grateful for. These can be big or small things, such as a supportive friend, a sunny day, or a good cup of coffee.

   What are you grateful for?

   Example: *(1) The incredible sense of well-being I felt following a brisk 20-minute walk before breakfast this morning. (2) My mother, who approves wholeheartedly of my recent lifestyle changes. (3) No waiting in line at the grocery store.*

   (1) _____

   (2) _____

   (3) _____

4. Next, write down one thing you could have done differently today or this week. Be honest with yourself, but also be kind and gentle.

What could you have done better?

Example: *I could have prioritized getting enough sleep better this week.*

_____

_____

_____

_____

5. Reflect on what you wrote down in Step 4 above. Next, write down what steps you can take to do better. Remember to break down any goals into small, achievable ones.

How should I improve on what I wrote down in Step 4?

Examples: *I should stop browsing the news and social media sites on my phone when I go to bed.*

_____

_____

_____

_____

6. Finish the exercise by setting an intention for the next day or week. This could be a goal you want to achieve, a habit you want to develop, or a positive attitude you want to cultivate.

What is your intention for tomorrow?

Example: *I will stop browsing the news and social media sites on my phone tonight. Tomorrow, I will buy a puzzle book to take to bed in case I can't sleep right away.*

_____

_____

_____

_____

What is your intention for next week?

Example: *I intend to start a sleep routine.*

_____

_____

_____

_____

Remember, reflection and gratitude are powerful tools for cultivating a positive mindset and reducing stress and anxiety. By taking a few minutes each day to reflect on the good things in your life and set positive intentions, you can improve your overall well-being and increase your resilience in the face of challenges.

Conclusion

""Believe you can, and you're halfway there."
— Theodore Roosevelt

Emotional eating may not be an official "disorder," but that does not mean healing from it is easy. Why? Because it is never easy to face one's emotions and address the reasons—the real reasons—behind them. However, as someone who has relied on food for comfort for many years, I can say from experience that there is hope. Believe in yourself, do the work and you WILL recover from emotional eating and feel better.

In my quest to heal from my mental health difficulties and emotional eating, I have read many books, tried many tips, talked to a few psychotherapists, and even studied psychology. Through it all, I discovered Dr. Marsha Linehan's Dialectical Behavior Therapy (DBT) to be crucial to my recovery. I hope you find it as beneficial as I have.

Here is a quick recap of what we covered in this book:

- Understanding Emotional Eating: emotional eating is coping with emotions or situations and has nearly nothing to do with food or physical hunger.
- Dialectical Behavior Therapy: DBT primary concepts (Acceptance and Change) and its primary skills (Mindfulness, Distress Tolerance, Emotion Regulation, and Interpersonal Effectiveness).
- Mindfulness: the DBT skill that teaches awareness and how mindful eating (eating without judgment or distraction) can help you develop a healthier relationship with food.

- <u>Distress Tolerance</u>: the DBT skill that teaches you how to survive a crisis. This is what you need to overcome moments when you feel a strong impulse or urge to reach for food to cope with your emotions.

- <u>Emotion Regulation</u>: the DBT skill that teaches you how to recognize and manage your emotions effectively. It is what you need to understand WHY you want to reach for food and why doing so is unhelpful in addressing the emotions and situations causing you to emotionally eat.

- <u>Interpersonal Effectiveness</u>: the DBT skill that teaches you how to make conversations and interactions effective. "Effective" means being more successful in getting what you want from a conversation.

- <u>Developing Healthy Habits</u>: this chapter discusses how taking care of your physical and emotional well-being helps prevent emotional eating. It discusses the importance of developing healthier food and eating habits, meal planning and prepping, incorporating exercise into your life, and dealing with everyday stress.

- <u>Building a Support System</u>: this chapter provides important tips on preventing possible self-sabotaging thoughts and actions and building an amazing internal (self) and external (others) support system.

- <u>Dealing with Setbacks and Relapses</u>: this section helps you prevent setbacks and how to bounce back from them when they do happen.

- <u>Maintaining Long-Term Success</u>: this section provides tips on maintaining a healthy relationship with food and recovering from emotional eating for good.

Appendix

Emotional Eating Self-Assessment Quiz

This emotional eating self-assessment quiz is meant to help you determine if you tend to eat in response to emotions rather than physical hunger.

Important: Please note that the results of this quiz are not intended to be a substitute for professional medical advice, diagnosis, or treatment. It is solely for informational and educational purposes. It should not be used as a basis for any decision or action regarding your health. If you are experiencing any symptoms or concerns related to emotional eating, please seek the advice of a qualified healthcare professional.

Please answer the questions below to the best of your ability.

1) **Do you find yourself eating more when you feel stressed, anxious, or upset?**
   a) Yes, all the time
   b) Sometimes
   c) Rarely
   d) Never

2) **Do you tend to eat even when you are not hungry?**
   a) Yes, all the time
   b) Sometimes
   c) Rarely
   d) Never

3) Do you feel guilty or ashamed after eating emotionally?

   a) Yes, all the time

   b) Sometimes

   c) Rarely

   d) Never

4) Do you eat to distract yourself from unpleasant emotions?

   a) Yes, all the time

   b) Sometimes

   c) Rarely

   d) Never

5) Do you eat when you are bored?

   a) Yes, all the time

   b) Sometimes

   c) Rarely

   d) Never

6) Do you find yourself eating more when you are alone?

   a) Yes, all the time

   b) Sometimes

   c) Rarely

   d) Never

7) Do you tend to eat quickly and not really taste your food?

   a) Yes, all the time

   b) Sometimes

   c) Rarely

   d) Never

8) Do you crave specific foods when you are feeling emotional?

a) Yes, all the time

b) Sometimes

c) Rarely

d) Never

9) Do you eat to reward yourself?

a) Yes, all the time

b) Sometimes

c) Rarely

d) Never

10)   Do you feel like you cannot control your eating when you start?

a) Yes, all the time

b) Sometimes

c) Rarely

d) Never

11) Do you feel like your emotions are driving your eating habits?

a) Yes, all the time

b) Sometimes

c) Rarely

d) Never

12)   Do you often eat until you feel uncomfortably full?

a) Yes, all the time

b) Sometimes

c) Rarely

d) Never

Scoring:

You can score the quiz by assigning the following point values to each answer:

- Always - 3 points
- Often - 2 points
- Sometimes - 1 point
- Never - 0 points

What your total score indicates:

- 0-5 points: Low likelihood of emotional eating
- 6-11 points: Mild likelihood of emotional eating
- 12-23 points: Moderate likelihood of emotional eating
- 24-36 points: High likelihood of emotional eating

The Clean Your Plate Syndrome

The Clean Your Plate (CYP) mentality refers to the idea that one should eat all the food on their plate, regardless of whether they are still hungry or not. Also called "consumption closure," this mentality is often instilled in individuals from a young age to prevent wasting food and encourage gratitude for having enough to eat.

I can definitely relate to the CYP mentality. We are constantly reminded of the significance of avoiding food waste in China. And because my parents grew up poor, this was a prevalent theme in our household during meals. A Chinese teacher once told me that her mother said every grain of rice she did not eat would turn into a mole on her face!

Unfortunately, the CYP mentality can lead to emotional eating because food is now closely linked to feelings of economy and gratitude rather than fuel for the body. And if you do not comply, feelings of guilt or shame may follow. This, again, promotes the emotional eating cycle. So, if you have a CYP mentality like me, here are some tips to help you stop it.

Top 10 Tips to Stop Cleaning Your Plate

1) **Take 5.** Develop the habit of doing the <u>Take 5</u> breathing exercise (page 39) before eating. It will relax your nervous system and improve your digestion and metabolism. It will also center you and make you more mindful of what you put on your plate and in your mouth. (If you cannot do the whole five minutes, do five breath cycles before eating.)

2) **Do not feel guilty about not cleaning your plate.** There is no need to finish everything on your plate. If you are concerned about wastage, do not be. Save leftovers for later or compost any excess food.

3) **Consider the consequences.** Remind yourself that overeating leads to discomfort. Also, research shows that the CYP mentality can lead to larger waistlines.[63] By not finishing your plate, you are practicing self-care.

4) **Use smaller plates**. Smaller plates mean less food to put on them. This way, you are "cleaning your plate" without necessarily overeating.

5) **Serve yourself smaller portions**. When serving yourself, start with smaller portions. Avoid returning for seconds until you have given yourself time to assess whether you are still physically hungry. When dining out or ordering in, ask for smaller portions. In Thailand and Japan, asking for less rice or noodles is common. This way, you remove the chance of ending up with more food than you need.

6) **Slow down and savor your food**. Eat slowly and mindfully. (See also <u>Mindful Eating</u>, page 45.) Give your brain a chance to tell you that you are full.

7) **Do not eat in front of distractions**. Avoid eating while working on your computer, watching TV, or checking your mobile phone. These activities can distract you from your food and cause you to get second helpings you do not need.

8) **Pay attention to your hunger cues**. Listen to your body and stop eating when you feel full. To avoid CYP guilt, remind yourself that leaving food on your plate is okay if you are already satisfied.

9) **Practice saying, "No, thank you."** Politely decline offers for more food or dessert if you feel full or satisfied. If someone insists and still puts food on your plate, leave it. If they ignore your "no," then feel free to ignore their actions. This is also a sign for them to take your objections seriously next time.

10) **Doggy bag it!** If you are eating out and the serving size is too big, do not feel compelled to finish your food. Ask for a doggy bag instead.

How to Establish a Sleep Routine

Sleep is one of the most underrated components of a healthy lifestyle. We take it for granted, not realizing how much harm we do ourselves by not getting the recommended 7 to 9 hours of sleep we should have each night.

One of the best ways to get the quality sleep we need is to establish a sleep routine. Following are some tips to accomplish this.

1. **Go to bed and wake up at the same time daily** to establish a regular sleep rhythm.

2. **Reserve your bed for sleep and romance.**

3. **Establish a clutter-free, peaceful, tranquil environment that promotes sleep**. Your bedroom should be a haven of peace and tranquility at the end of a long day.

4. Create **complete darkness and silence** (eyeshades and earplugs are useful instruments). Remove or cover any illuminated clocks or digital electronic displays.

5. **Get at least twenty minutes of sunlight exposure daily**, especially first thing in the morning. Sunlight penetrates your eyes and causes your brain to release hormones such as melatonin, which is essential for good sleep cycles and mood balance. If you live somewhere where the sun is scarce at certain times of the year, like I do in Canada, consider investing in a light therapy lamp to help reset your circadian rhythm.

6. **Do not eat within three hours of going to bed.** A large dinner before bedtime will result in a restless night's sleep. Energy will be diverted to

digesting your meal rather than the repair and mending that is supposed to occur at night. Eating too late is also a foolproof method to gain weight since your body will store the food (as fat) rather than burn it.

7. **Avoid using bright, stimulating screens before going to bed.** Using electronic gadgets in bed changes the normal sleep molecules in your brain. Do not check your e-mail, read on your iPad, or check your phone. Watching television straight before bed can also greatly disrupt sleep. If you must use it to check something important, ensure your device has a blue light filtering app installed, such as Twilight for your phone or f.lux for your laptop.

8. **Allow an hour (or at least twenty minutes) for total relaxation.** To prepare your thoughts for sleep, listen to quiet music or read something pleasant in bed. You might also try some simple yoga stretches or breathing exercises.

9. **Make a list of your concerns.** Are you ruminating or worried about something? Get up and start writing them down. Mentally unload whatever is disturbing your sleep, and then return to bed. (**Tip**: Keep a notepad or journal beside your bed for such moments.)

10. **Cool down your bedroom.** Room temperatures between 60 and 67°F are ideal for Rapid Eye Movement (REM) sleep, which occurs during the stages of dreaming, learning, memory, emotional processing, and healthy brain growth. If your room is too hot or cold, you'll wake up frequently, preventing you from attaining REM and deep, restorative sleep.

11. **Warm up your core.** This boosts your core temperature and aids in activating the right chemistry for sleep. A hot water bottle, heating pad, or your partner's warm body can help.

12. **Avoid sleep-interfering drugs**. Sedatives such as antihistamines, stimulants, cold medications, steroids, and caffeine-containing headache remedies should be avoided. These medications eventually disrupt natural sleep patterns.

How to Support an Emotional Eater

If you have a friend or loved one trying to heal from emotional eating, know your support is an important factor in their journey. Here are some of the ways you can support them:

1. **Acknowledge how difficult their journey is for them.** Understanding and support come after acknowledgment. Often, it is difficult for people to offer support because they cannot relate to the issue. However, keep in mind that this is *their* story, *their* journey. You need not be an emotional eater to love and support one.

2. **Be non-judgmental and empathetic.** It is essential to be compassionate towards your friend or loved one. Do not judge their previous choices and criticize them, but support their intention to improve.

3. **Listen actively.** Show genuine concern and support by encouraging them to talk about their emotions, what triggers their emotional eating, and what struggles they are going through in their journey. Pay attention to what they are expressing, and avoid interrupting them as they speak. Remember, the goal of active listening is to walk away from the conversation with a complete understanding of the other person's point of view.

4. **Help them identify healthy coping mechanisms.** Emotional eaters may not be aware of alternative ways to deal with their emotions. Help them identify healthy coping mechanisms like exercising, meditating, journaling, starting a new hobby, etc. If possible for you, offer your time. For example, if they are shy or unsure about joining a nearby gym, offer to join and attend classes with them.

5. **Encourage healthy eating habits**. Be a positive influence by suggesting nutritious meals and snacks that are satisfying and healthy. Encourage them to eat slowly, savor their food, and stop when full (mindful eating). If you are not into these things yourself, the best thing you can do is to at least not be an enabler of emotional eating. For example, avoid consuming unhealthy foods and drinks in front of them; refrain from mentioning people or events that you know trigger them, etc.

6. **Offer the support they need**. Let your friend or loved one know that you are there to support them in the way they want to be supported. (See the different kinds of support you can offer on page 124.)

    You can also ask them open-ended questions such as "*How can I help you?*", "*What do you need from me?*" or "*What are you struggling with the most?*" to explore the support that would benefit them the most and that you can give.

    But what if your friend or loved one says they do not want your help? Respect their wishes but **keep checking in on them**. Even if they avoid the subject, you can still support them by being there. For instance, you could ask them if they want to go for a walk, watch a movie, join a class together, etc. If you feel they are more open to discussing their struggles, you can ask questions like, "*How are you? Anything you want to share?*" or "*I won't nag you. Just let me know if you need anything, okay?*"

    Here are some other messages your friend or loved one might appreciate hearing from you.

    I'm here to listen.
    You're not alone.

Your feelings are valid.

It's not just about willpower.

Your health and well-being matter.

I don't understand it, but I'll be here anyway.

Do what makes you happy.

You're stronger than you think.

You can do this!

You don't have to do this alone.

It is admirable that you want to help someone recovering from emotional eating, but please keep the following in mind.

Support does not mean taking over. When you support someone, you offer guidance, encouragement, and assistance—that is it. Empowering them to make their own decisions and taking ownership of their journey is crucial. Taking over completely can inadvertently undermine their sense of autonomy, self-efficacy, and personal growth.

In contrast, by allowing them to navigate their challenges and make their own choices, you are enabling them to develop problem-solving skills, resilience, and independence. It also shows respect for their abilities and acknowledges their capacity to handle their affairs.

Practice self-care. Supporting someone trying to unlearn a maladaptive behavior can be draining and affect your mental, emotional, and physical well-being. As such, be sure to take care of yourself by practicing self-care activities that you find effective, such as meditating, exercising, getting enough sleep, etc. This also means taking a break from your friend or loved one when needed. However, please do not ghost them. Instead, say something like, *"I need some* time off, so I won't be available for a while. However, know I support you, so you'll hear from me when I return."

Review Request

If you enjoyed this book or found it useful...

I'd like to ask you for a quick favor:

Please share your thoughts and leave a quick REVIEW. Your feedback matters and helps me make improvements to provide the best books possible.

Reviews are so helpful to both readers and authors, so any help would be greatly appreciated! You can leave a review here:

https://tinyurl.com/dbt-eating-review

Or by scanning the QR code below:

Also, please join my ARC team to get early access to my releases.

https://barretthuang.com/arc-team/

THANK YOU!

Further Reading

Be sure to check out my other bestselling DBT books in the Mental Health Therapy series. Here are some of the titles you can find:

- DBT Workbook for Adults
- DBT Workbook for Kids
- DBT Workbook for Teens
- The DBT Anger Management Workbook
- DBT Workbook for PTSD
- DBT Workbook for BPD
- DBT Workbook for Depression

You can get them here:

https://tinyurl.com/mental-health-therapy

About the Author

Barrett Huang is an author and businessman. Barrett spent years discovering the best ways to manage his OCD, overcoming his anxiety, and learning to embrace life. Through his writing, he hopes to share his knowledge with readers, empowering people of all backgrounds with the tools and strategies they need to improve their mental wellbeing and be happy and healthy.

When not writing or running his business, Barrett loves to spend his time studying. He has majored in psychology and completed the DBT skills certificate course by Dr. Marsha Linehan. Barrett's idol is Bruce Lee, who said, "The key to immortality is first living a life worth remembering."

Learn more about Barrett's books here:

https://barretthuang.com/

Index

Acceptance + Change, 34, 133
Acceptance and Change, 26, 27, 142
Anxiety, 10, 11, 17, 21, 26, 52, 74, 80, 110, 111, 119, 141
Binge eating disorder, 14
Binge-eating, 15
Borderline Personality Disorder, 22, 26
Boredom, 8, 21, 53, 59, 65, 74, 83, 90, 116
Boundaries, 92, 95, 97, 126, 134
BPD, 22, 26, 27
CBT, 10, 11, 26
Chronic diseases, 24, 25
Clean Your Plate, 21, 77, 148
Cognitive Behavior Therapy, 10
CYP, 148, 149, 150
DBT, 11, 12, 26, 27, 28, 34, 35, 36, 92, 108, 133, 142, 143
DEARMAN, 98
Decision fatigue, 112, 118
Depression, 10, 11, 17, 21, 22, 26, 80, 110
Desire to change, 31, 33
Dialectical Behavior Therapy, 11, 12, 20, 26, 142
Dieting history, 21
Distress, 34, 35, 52, 53, 83, 97, 123, 133, 142, 143
Distress tolerance, 52, 53
Emotion regulation, 34, 35, 65, 122, 123, 133, 142, 143
Emotional eater, 14, 23, 34, 37, 49, 65, 66, 95, 154
Emotional eating, 7, 8, 11, 12, 13, 14, 15, 16, 18, 19, 20, 21, 22, 23, 24, 25, 27, 28, 29, 31, 37, 44, 49, 52, 53, 54, 65, 66, 67, 70, 74, 75, 76, 77, 78, 80, 83, 88, 89, 90, 91, 92, 93, 95, 104, 105, 107, 108, 109, 110, 111, 112, 115, 117, 119, 121, 122, 124, 127, 130, 131, 132, 133, 134, 136, 138, 142, 143, 144, 147, 148, 154, 155, 156
Emotional hunger, 15, 16, 59, 63
Emotional Mind, 50
Emotional support, 92, 124
FAST, 104
Fatigue, 23
Food journal, 75, 76, 111
GAD, 8, 10, 11, 22
General Anxiety Disorder, 8, 22
Genetics, 22
GIVE, 102
Gochisosama, 42
Gratitude, 42, 80, 94, 120, 138, 139, 141, 148
Grounding Grid, 57
Happy eating, 53
Immune system, 25
Inflammation, 17, 23, 24, 25
Insomnia, 24
Intellectual support, 124
Interpersonal effectiveness, 34, 35, 91, 92, 94, 133, 142, 143
Itadakimasu, 42
Learned behavior, 12, 19, 91
Loneliness, 7, 8, 9, 53, 74, 80, 90, 93
Low self-esteem, 20
Marsha M. Linehan, 26, 27, 34, 52, 142
Meal planning, 88, 112, 113, 123, 132, 135, 137, 143
Meal prepping, 88, 112, 113, 114, 115, 132, 135, 137, 143
Mental health, 22
Mindful eating, 34, 41, 42, 43, 44, 108, 117, 128, 131, 134, 135, 142, 155
Mindfulness, 34, 35, 37, 44, 100, 117, 123, 128, 133, 142
Mindless eating, 23
Moral support, 124
Non-judgmental, 42, 154

Nutrient deficiencies, 24
Obsessive-Compulsive Disorder, 8
OCD, 8, 10, 11
Opposite Action, 83, 84
Paired muscle relaxation, 64
Physical health, 22, 23
Physical hunger, 13, 14, 15, 16, 21, 48, 110, 142, 144
Physical support, 124
Poor digestion, 23
Post-Traumatic Stress Disorder, 22
Psychotherapy, 10, 11
PTSD, 22
Radical acceptance, 27, 28, 29, 31, 33, 130
Reasonable Mind, 50
Reflection, 120, 138, 139, 141
Relapses, 127, 131, 132, 134
Resource support, 124
Self-awareness, 77, 136
Self-care, 94, 122, 131, 149, 156
Self-compassion, 66, 69, 74, 94, 111, 121, 122, 130
Self-esteem, 93
Self-forgiveness, 66, 67, 71, 130
Self-sabotage, 121, 122
Self-validation, 66, 67, 74
Setbacks, 12, 127, 130, 132, 134, 143
Skin problems, 24
Sleep routine, 89, 118, 151
STOP, 59, 128
Stress, 14, 20, 52, 117, 118
Stress eating, 14
Support circle, 123
Support system, 126, 134, 143
Take 5, 45, 57, 63, 97, 118, 149
TASTE, 48

The Happiness Advantage, 80
TIPP, 62, 118
Trauma, 20
Weight gain, 23
Willpower, 18, 19, 20, 72, 156
Wise Mind, 49, 51
Worksheet: 4-7-8 Breathing, 40
Worksheet: Belly Breathing, 38
Worksheet: Communicating Boundaries, 95
Worksheet: DEARMAN, 98
Worksheet: Desire to Change, 32
Worksheet: FAST, 104
Worksheet: GIVE, 102
Worksheet: Identifying Your Emotional Triggers, 75
Worksheet: Mindful Eating, 45
Worksheet: Opposite Action, 83
Worksheet: PLEASE, 88
Worksheet: Radical Acceptance, 29
Worksheet: Radical Acceptance and Desire to Change, 33
Worksheet: Reflection and Gratitude, 139
Worksheet: Self-Compassion, 68
Worksheet: Self-Forgiveness, 70
Worksheet: Self-Soothe Using Your Five Senses, 55
Worksheet: Self-Validation, 72
Worksheet: STOP, 59
Worksheet: Take 5, 39
Worksheet: TASTE, 48
Worksheet: The Grounding Grid, 57
Worksheet: The Happiness Habit, 80
Worksheet: TIPP, 62
Worksheet: Wise Mind, 49

References

1 American Psychiatric Association Publishing. (2022). *Diagnostic and statistical manual of mental disorders, fifth edition text revision: Dsm-5-Tr.*

2 Firth, J., Gangwisch, J. E., Borsini, A., Wootton, R. E., & Mayer, E. A. (2020). Food and mood: How do diet and nutrition affect mental wellbeing? *BMJ*, m2382. https://doi.org/10.1136/bmj.m2382

3 ElBarazi, A., & Tikamdas, R. (2023). Association between university student junk food consumption and mental health. *Nutrition and Health*, 026010602311514. https://doi.org/10.1177/02601060231151480

4 Wang, Q.-P., Lin, Y. Q., Zhang, L., Wilson, Y. A., Oyston, L. J., Cotterell, J., Qi, Y., Khuong, T. M., Bakhshi, N., Planchenault, Y., Browman, D. T., Lau, M. T., Cole, T. A., Wong, A. C. N., Simpson, S. J., Cole, A. R., Penninger, J. M., Herzog, H., & Neely, G. G. (2016). Sucralose promotes food intake through NPY and a neuronal fasting response. *Cell Metabolism*, *24*(1), 75–90. https://doi.org/10.1016/j.cmet.2016.06.010

5 Herle, M., Fildes, A., & Llewellyn, C. H. (2018). Emotional eating is learned not inherited in children, regardless of obesity risk. *Pediatric Obesity*, *13*(10), 628–631. https://doi.org/10.1111/ijpo.12428

6 Edwin Thanarajah, S., DiFeliceantonio, A. G., Albus, K., Kuzmanovic, B., Rigoux, L., Iglesias, S., Hanßen, R., Schlamann, M., Cornely, O. A., Brüning, J. C., Tittgemeyer, M., & Small, D. M. (2023). Habitual daily intake of a sweet and fatty snack modulates reward processing in humans. *Cell Metabolism*, *35*(4). https://doi.org/10.1016/j.cmet.2023.02.015

7 Schnepper, R., Georgii, C., Eichin, K., Arend, A.-K., Wilhelm, F. H., Vögele, C., Lutz, A. P., van Dyck, Z., & Blechert, J. (2020). Fight, flight, – or grab a bite! trait emotional and restrained eating style predicts food cue responding under negative emotions. *Frontiers in Behavioral Neuroscience, 14*. https://doi.org/10.3389/fnbeh.2020.00091

8 Yin, H. H., & Knowlton, B. J. (2006). The role of the basal ganglia in habit formation. *Nature Reviews Neuroscience*, *7*(6), 464–476. https://doi.org/10.1038/nrn1919

9 Carpio-Arias, T. V., Solís Manzano, A. M., Sandoval, V., Vinueza-Veloz, A. F., Rodríguez Betancourt, A., Betancourt Ortíz, S. L., & Vinueza-Veloz, M. F.

(2022). Relationship between perceived stress and emotional eating. A Cross Sectional Study. *Clinical Nutrition ESPEN, 49,* 314–318. https://doi.org/10.1016/j.clnesp.2022.03.030

10 Shehata, W. M., & Abdeldaim, D. E. (2023). Emotional eating in relation to psychological stress during COVID-19 pandemic: A cross-sectional study in Faculty of Medicine, Tanta University, Egypt. *BMC Public Health, 23*(1). https://doi.org/10.1186/s12889-023-15177-x

11 Zellner, D. A., Loaiza, S., Gonzalez, Z., Pita, J., Morales, J., Pecora, D., & Wolf, A. (2006). Food selection changes under stress. *Physiology & Behavior, 87*(4), 789–793. https://doi.org/10.1016/j.physbeh.2006.01.014

12 Talbot, L. S., Maguen, S., Epel, E. S., Metzler, T. J., & Neylan, T. C. (2013). Posttraumatic stress disorder is associated with emotional eating. *Journal of Traumatic Stress, 26*(4), 521–525. https://doi.org/10.1002/jts.21824

13 Schroeder, K., Schuler, B. R., Kobulsky, J. M., & Sarwer, D. B. (2021). The association between adverse childhood experiences and childhood obesity: A systematic review. *Obesity Reviews, 22*(7). https://doi.org/10.1111/obr.13204

14 Hoare, P., & Cosgrove, L. (1998). Eating habits, body-esteem and self-esteem in Scottish children and adolescents. *Journal of Psychosomatic Research, 45*(5), 425–431. https://doi.org/10.1016/s0022-3999(98)00025-7

15 Izydorczyk, B., Sitnik-Warchulska, K., Lizińczyk, S., & Lipiarz, A. (2019). Psychological predictors of unhealthy eating attitudes in young adults. *Frontiers in Psychology, 10.* https://doi.org/10.3389/fpsyg.2019.00590

16 Werneck, G. de, & De Oliveira, D. R. (2021). Autoestima e Estereótipos do Comer Emocional. *Revista Psicologia e Saúde,* 117–130. https://doi.org/10.20435/pssa.v13i3.1157

17 Goossens, L., Braet, C., Van Vlierberghe, L., & Mels, S. (2009). Loss of control over eating in overweight youngsters: The role of anxiety, depression and emotional eating. *European Eating Disorders Review, 17*(1), 68–78. https://doi.org/10.1002/erv.892

18 Konttinen, H., van Strien, T., Männistö, S., Jousilahti, P., & Haukkala, A. (2019). Depression, emotional eating and long-term weight changes: A population-based prospective study. *International Journal of Behavioral Nutrition and Physical Activity, 16*(1). https://doi.org/10.1186/s12966-019-0791-8

19 Burnatowska, E., Surma, S., & Olszanecka-Glinianowicz, M. (2022). Relationship between mental health and emotional eating during the covid-19 pandemic: A systematic review. *Nutrients, 14*(19), 3989. https://doi.org/10.3390/nu14193989

20 Moynihan, A. B., Tilburg, W. A., Igou, E. R., Wisman, A., Donnelly, A. E., & Mulcaire, J. B. (2015). Eaten up by boredom: Consuming food to escape awareness of the bored self. *Frontiers in Psychology, 6.* https://doi.org/10.3389/fpsyg.2015.00369

21 Ahlich, E., & Rancourt, D. (2022). Boredom proneness, interoception, and emotional eating. *Appetite, 178*, 106167. https://doi.org/10.1016/j.appet.2022.106167

22 Higgs, S., & Thomas, J. (2016). Social influences on eating. *Current Opinion in Behavioral Sciences, 9*, 1–6. https://doi.org/10.1016/j.cobeha.2015.10.005

23 Nilsson , F. (2022, June 20). *Emotional eating: How culture, generation and Emotion Drive Food Purchase Decisions, 91% of Aussies have more intense food category view post-covid, big opportunities for FMCG brands: Mi3. Welcome to Mi3.* Retrieved April 1, 2023, from https://www.mi-3.com.au/20-06-2022/emotional-eating-how-culture-generation-and-emotion-drive-food-purchase-decisions-91

24 Ilyuk, V., Block, L., & Haws, K. L. (2019). Justifying by "healthifying": When expected satisfaction from consumption closure increases the desire to eat more and biases health perceptions of unhealthy leftovers. *Appetite, 133*, 138–146. https://doi.org/10.1016/j.appet.2018.10.030

25 Bresch, A., Rullmann, M., Luthardt, J., Becker, G. A., Patt, M., Ding, Y.-S., Hilbert, A., Sabri, O., & Hesse, S. (2017). Hunger and disinhibition but not cognitive restraint are associated with central norepinephrine transporter availability. *Appetite, 117*, 270–274. https://doi.org/10.1016/j.appet.2017.06.020

26 Betancourt-Núñez, A., Torres-Castillo, N., Martínez-López, E., De Loera-Rodríguez, C. O., Durán-Barajas, E., Márquez-Sandoval, F., Bernal-Orozco, M. F., Garaulet, M., & Vizmanos, B. (2022). Emotional eating and dietary patterns: Reflecting food choices in people with and without abdominal obesity. *Nutrients, 14*(7), 1371. https://doi.org/10.3390/nu14071371

27 Javaras, K. N., Laird, N. M., Reichborn-Kjennerud, T., Bulik, C. M., Pope, H. G., & Hudson, J. I. (2008). Familiality and heritability of binge eating

disorder: Results of a case-control family study and a twin study. *International Journal of Eating Disorders, 41*(2), 174–179. https://doi.org/10.1002/eat.20484

28 van Strien, T., Snoek, H. M., van der Zwaluw, C. S., & Engels, R. C. M. E. (2010). Parental control and the dopamine D2 receptor gene (DRD2) interaction on emotional eating in adolescence. *Appetite, 54*(2), 255–261. https://doi.org/10.1016/j.appet.2009.11.006

29 Kinney, J. W., Bemiller, S. M., Murtishaw, A. S., Leisgang, A. M., Salazar, A. M., & Lamb, B. T. (2018). Inflammation as a central mechanism in alzheimer's disease. *Alzheimer's & Dementia: Translational Research & Clinical Interventions, 4*(1), 575–590. https://doi.org/10.1016/j.trci.2018.06.014

30 Linehan, M. (2021). *Building a Life Worth Living: A Memoir*. Random House.

31 Roosen, M. A., Safer, D., Adler, S. N., Cebolla, A., & Strien, T. van. (2012, November 21). *Group dialectical behavior therapy adapted for obese emotional eaters; a pilot study*. Vrije Universiteit Amsterdam. Retrieved April 1, 2023, from https://research.vu.nl/en/publications/group-dialectical-behavior-therapy-adapted-for-obese-emotional-ea

32 Rahmani, M., Omidi, A., Asemi, Z., & Akbari, H. (2018). The effect of dialectical behaviour therapy on binge eating, difficulties in emotion regulation and BMI in overweight patients with binge-eating disorder: A randomized controlled trial. *Mental Health & Prevention, 9*, 13–18. https://doi.org/10.1016/j.mhp.2017.11.002

33 Brown, T. A., Wisniewski, L., & Anderson, L. K. (2020). Dialectical behavior therapy for eating disorders: State of the research and New Directions. *Eating Disorders, 28*(2), 97–100. https://doi.org/10.1080/10640266.2020.1728204

34 Lee, A. (2020, April 7). *Why change is hard ... and good*. Ideas & Insights. Retrieved February 1, 2023, from https://www8.gsb.columbia.edu/articles/ideas-work/why-change-hard-and-good

35 Olson, K. L. L., & Emery, C. F. (2015). Mindfulness and weight loss. *Psychosomatic Medicine, 77*(1), 59–67. https://doi.org/10.1097/psy.0000000000000127

36 Arch, J. J., Brown, K. W., Goodman, R. J., Della Porta, M. D., Kiken, L. G., & Tillman, S. (2016). Enjoying food without caloric cost: The impact of brief mindfulness on laboratory eating outcomes. *Behaviour Research and Therapy, 79*, 23–34. https://doi.org/10.1016/j.brat.2016.02.002

37 Zuraikat, F. M., Makarem, N., Liao, M., St-Onge, M. P., & Aggarwal, B. (2020). Measures of poor sleep quality are associated with higher energy intake and poor diet quality in a diverse sample of women from the Go Red for Women Strategically Focused Research Network. *Journal of the American Heart Association, 9*(4). https://doi.org/10.1161/jaha.119.014587

38 Järvelä-Reijonen, E., Järvinen, S., Karhunen, L., Föhr, T., Myllymäki, T., Sairanen, E., Lindroos, S., Peuhkuri, K., Hallikainen, M., Pihlajamäki, J., Puttonen, S., Korpela, R., Ermes, M., Lappalainen, R., Kujala, U. M., Kolehmainen, M., & Laitinen, J. (2021). Sleep-time physiological recovery is associated with eating habits in distressed working-age Finns with overweight: Secondary analysis of a randomised controlled trial. *Journal of Occupational Medicine and Toxicology, 16*(1). https://doi.org/10.1186/s12995-021-00310-6

39 Moore, S. (2021, December 7). Adapted from *What is 'mindful eating'?* NC Cooperative Extension News. Retrieved April 1, 2023, from https://stokes.ces.ncsu.edu/2021/12/what-is-mindful-eating/

40 Carpio-Arias, T. V., Solís Manzano, A. M., Sandoval, V., Vinueza-Veloz, A. F., Rodríguez Betancourt, A., Betancourt Ortíz, S. L., & Vinueza-Veloz, M. F. (2022). Relationship between perceived stress and emotional eating. A Cross Sectional Study. *Clinical Nutrition ESPEN, 49*, 314–318. https://doi.org/10.1016/j.clnesp.2022.03.030

41 Shehata, W. M., & Abdeldaim, D. E. (2023). Emotional eating in relation to psychological stress during COVID-19 pandemic: A cross-sectional study in Faculty of Medicine, Tanta University, Egypt. *BMC Public Health, 23*(1). https://doi.org/10.1186/s12889-023-15177-x

42 Bongers, P., Jansen, A., Havermans, R., Roefs, A., & Nederkoorn, C. (2013). Happy eating. the underestimated role of overeating in a positive mood. *Appetite, 67*, 74–80. https://doi.org/10.1016/j.appet.2013.03.017

43 Hamilton, D. (2021, July 26). *Use your body to change how you feel.* David R Hamilton PHD. Retrieved April 1, 2023, from https://drdavidhamilton.com/use-your-body-to-change-how-you-feel/ s

44 Oliver, G., Wardle, J., & Gibson, E. L. (2000). Stress and food choice: A laboratory study. *Psychosomatic Medicine*, *62*(6), 853–865. https://doi.org/10.1097/00006842-200011000-00016

45 van Strien, T., Cebolla, A., Etchemendy, E., Gutiérrez-Maldonado, J., Ferrer-García, M., Botella, C., & Baños, R. (2013). Emotional eating and food intake after sadness and joy. *Appetite*, *66*, 20–25. https://doi.org/10.1016/j.appet.2013.02.016

46 Achor, S. (2018). *The happiness advantage: How a positive brain fuels success in work and life*. Currency.

47 Pally, R., & Olds, D. (2018). Emotional processing: The mind-body connection. *The Mind-Brain Relationship*, 73–104. https://doi.org/10.4324/9780429482465-4

48 *Healthy Eating Plate*. The Nutrition Source. (2023, January 31). Retrieved February 1, 2023, from https://www.hsph.harvard.edu/nutritionsource/healthy-eating-plate/

49 López-Cepero, A., Frisard, C., Mabry, G., Spruill, T., Mattei, J., Austin, S. B., Lemon, S. C., & Rosal, M. C. (2022). Association between poor sleep quality and emotional eating in US latinx adults and the mediating role of negative emotions. *Behavioral Sleep Medicine*, *21*(2), 162–171. https://doi.org/10.1080/15402002.2022.2060227

50 St-Onge, M.-P., Wolfe, S., Sy, M., Shechter, A., & Hirsch, J. (2013). Sleep restriction increases the neuronal response to unhealthy food in normal-weight individuals. *International Journal of Obesity*, *38*(3), 411–416. https://doi.org/10.1038/ijo.2013.114

51 Greer, S. M., Goldstein, A. N., & Walker, M. P. (2013). The impact of sleep deprivation on food desire in the human brain. *Nature Communications*, *4*(1). https://doi.org/10.1038/ncomms3259

52 Watson, N. F., Badr, M. S., Belenky, G., Bliwise, D. L., Buxton, O. M., Buysse, D., Dinges, D. F., Gangwisch, J., Grandner, M. A., Kushida, C., Malhotra, R. K., Martin, J. L., Patel, S. R., Quan, S., & Tasali, E. (2015). Recommended amount of sleep for a healthy adult: A joint consensus statement of the American Academy of Sleep Medicine and Sleep Research Society. *SLEEP*. https://doi.org/10.5665/sleep.4716

53 Christakis, N. A., & Fowler, J. H. (2007). The spread of obesity in a large social network over 32 years. *New England Journal of Medicine, 357*(4), 370–379. https://doi.org/10.1056/nejmsa066082

54 Armstrong, L. E., Ganio, M. S., Casa, D. J., Lee, E. C., McDermott, B. P., Klau, J. F., Jimenez, L., Le Bellego, L., Chevillotte, E., & Lieberman, H. R. (2012). Mild dehydration affects mood in healthy young women,. *The Journal of Nutrition, 142*(2), 382–388. https://doi.org/10.3945/jn.111.142000

55 Pross, N., Demazières, A., Girard, N., Barnouin, R., Metzger, D., Klein, A., Perrier, E., & Guelinckx, I. (2014). Effects of changes in water intake on mood of high and low drinkers. *PLoS ONE, 9*(4). https://doi.org/10.1371/journal.pone.0094754

56 *Dietary reference intakes for water, potassium, sodium, chloride, and sulfate dri.* (2005). National Academies Press.

57 Li, Y., Zhang, C., Li, S., & Zhang, D. (2020). Association between dietary protein intake and the risk of depressive symptoms in adults. *British Journal of Nutrition, 123*(11), 1290–1301. https://doi.org/10.1017/s0007114520000562

58 Gerber, M., Jakowski, S., Kellmann, M., Cody, R., Gygax, B., Ludyga, S., Müller, C., Ramseyer, S., & Beckmann, J. (2023). Macronutrient intake as a prospective predictor of depressive symptom severity: An exploratory study with Adolescent Elite Athletes. *Psychology of Sport and Exercise, 66,* 102387. https://doi.org/10.1016/j.psychsport.2023.102387

59 Jaret, P. (2022, November 22). *Daily Protein Requirements: Are You Getting Enough?*. WebMD. https://www.webmd.com/food-recipes/protein

60 Annesi, J. J., & Mareno, N. (2015). Indirect effects of exercise on emotional eating through psychological predictors of weight loss in women. *Appetite, 95,* 219–227. https://doi.org/10.1016/j.appet.2015.07.012

61 Smith, K. E., O'Connor, S. M., Mason, T. B., Wang, S., Dzubur, E., Crosby, R. D., Wonderlich, S. A., Salvy, S., Feda, D. M., & Roemmich, J. N. (2020). Associations between objective physical activity and emotional eating among adiposity-discordant siblings using ecological momentary assessment and accelerometers. *Pediatric Obesity, 16*(3). https://doi.org/10.1111/ijpo.12720

62 Okoye, A. (2023, March 10). *Benefits of working out before bed.* The Sleep Doctor. https://thesleepdoctor.com/exercise/benefits-of-exercise-for-sleep/

63 Raghunathan, R., & Chandrasekaran, D. (2020). The association between the attitude of food-waste-aversion and BMI: An exploration in India and the United States. *Journal of Consumer Psychology, 31*(1), 81–90. https://doi.org/10.1002/jcpy.1168

Printed in the USA
CPSIA information can be obtained
at www.ICGtesting.com
LVHW060722080923
757247LV00010B/241